HMH | (into) **Math**™

Volume 2

Modules 13–20

Currency and Coins Photos courtesy of United States Mint, Bureau of Engraving and Houghton Mifflin Harcourt

Printed in the U.S.A.

ISBN   978-0-358-00227-7

4 5 6 7 8 9 10   0868   28 27 26 25 24 23 22 21 20

4500801296   C D E F G

Dear Students and Families,

Welcome to *Into Math, Grade 3!* In this program, you will develop skills and make sense of mathematics by solving real-world problems, using hands-on tools and strategies, and collaborating with your classmates.

With the support of your teacher and by engaging with meaningful practice, you will learn to persevere when solving problems. *Into Math* will not only help you deepen your understanding of mathematics, but also build your confidence as a learner of mathematics.

Even more exciting, you will write all your ideas and solutions right in your book. In your *Into Math* book, writing and drawing on the pages will help you think deeply about what you are learning, help you truly understand math, and most important, you will become a confident user of mathematics!

Sincerely,
The Authors

Authors

Edward B. Burger, PhD
President, Southwestern University
Georgetown, Texas

Matthew R. Larson, PhD
Past-President, National Council
of Teachers of Mathematics
Lincoln Public Schools
Lincoln, Nebraska

Juli K. Dixon, PhD
Professor, Mathematics Education
University of Central Florida
Orlando, Florida

Steven J. Leinwand
Principal Research Analyst
American Institutes for Research
Washington, DC

Timothy D. Kanold, PhD
Mathematics Educator
Chicago, Illinois

Jennifer Lempp
Educational Consultant
Alexandria, Virginia

Consultants

English Language Development Consultant

Harold Asturias
Director, Center for Mathematics
Excellence and Equity
Lawrence Hall of Science, University of California
Berkeley, California

Program Consultant

David Dockterman, EdD
Lecturer, Harvard Graduate School of Education
Cambridge, Massachusetts

Blended Learning Consultant

Weston Kieschnick
Senior Fellow
International Center for Leadership in Education
Littleton, Colorado

STEM Consultants

Michael A. DiSpezio
Global Educator
North Falmouth, Massachusetts

Marjorie Frank
Science Writer and
Content-Area Reading Specialist
Brooklyn, New York

Bernadine Okoro
Access and Equity and
STEM Learning Advocate and Consultant
Washington, DC

Cary I. Sneider, PhD
Associate Research Professor
Portland State University
Portland, Oregon

Unit
4
Fractions

Unit Opener 349

MODULE 13 Understand Fractions as Numbers

○ Build Understanding   ○ Connect Concepts and Skills   ○ Apply and Practice

MODULE 16 Understand Equivalent Fractions

Build Understanding   Connect Concepts and Skills   Apply and Practice

Unit 5

Measurement and Data

MODULE 18 Represent and Interpret Data

○ Build Understanding   ○ Connect Concepts and Skills   ○ Apply and Practice

Unit 6 Geometry

Unit Opener 487

Build Understanding ⬤ Connect Concepts and Skills ⬤ Apply and Practice

Fractions

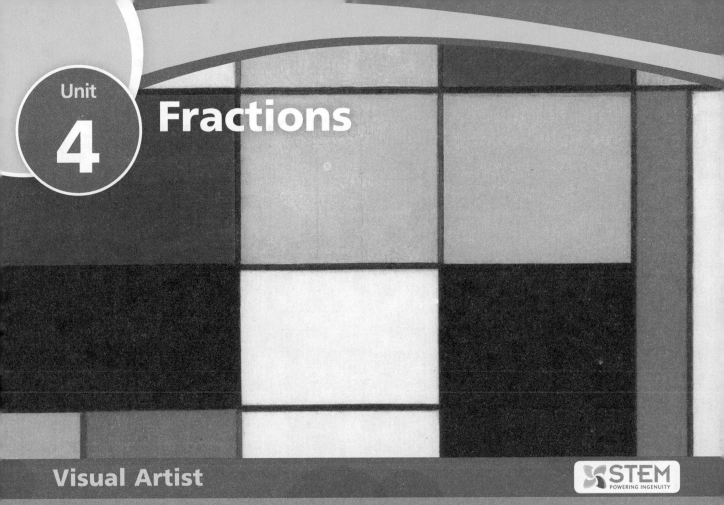

Visual Artist

⚘STEM
POWERING INGENUITY

Visual art is any art you can see—like photos, paintings, movies, and sculpture. You see the work of visual artists every day. All the posters, books, and photos you see are designed or made by visual artists!

Did you know that the world's oldest known works of art, cave paintings found in France, were made by visual artists who lived over 20,000 years ago?

The painting above was painted by a Dutch artist Piet Mondrian. Mondrian often painted differently-sized vertical and horizontal rectangles colored red, yellow, blue, white, and black. His paintings continue to inspire designs in furniture, lamps, fabrics, clothing, dinnerware, and more. There is even a map of the world painted with just Mondrian rectangles.

STEM Task:

Here is a puzzle inspired by Mondrian. Draw a square on grid paper that measures 10 units on each side. Can you divide the square into rectangles that each have a different size and shape? Color your rectangles red, blue, yellow, and black.

Learning Mindset
Strategic Help-Seeking
Identifies Sources of Help

We all use tools to help ourselves. A toothbrush is a tool to keep your teeth clean. What tools do you use to get to school? Do you walk or ride a bicycle? Or does someone drive you in a car or a bus? You also use tools for learning. The grid paper, pencil, and crayons or markers you used to design the puzzle inspired by Mondrian are also tools. Using the proper tools helps you work more efficiently.

Reflect

Q How did the instructions for your puzzle help you complete the task? Were the instructions effective tools for you?

Q How were the rectangles also tools? What other tools did you use?

© Houghton Mifflin Harcourt Publishing Company • Image Credit: ©Education & Exploration 3/Alamy

Understand Fractions as Numbers

HOW CAN I SHARE CLAY?

- You have a circle of blue clay.

- Your partner has a rectangle of yellow clay.

- You both want to share each color of clay equally.

- Draw a line that shows how your partner could cut the yellow clay so you both have the same amount.

- Draw a line that shows how you could cut the blue clay so you both have the same amount.

 Turn and Talk

- Share your drawings with other groups. How are the ways you cut the clay the same, and how are they different?

- Could the blue clay be shared equally among three friends? Explain.

Are You Ready?

Complete these problems to review prior concepts and
skills you will need for this module.

Halves and Fourths

1 Shade half of the rectangle.

2 Draw lines to show fourths.

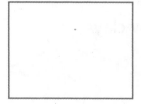
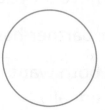

Equal Shares

3 Circle the shape that is divided into 4 equal shares.

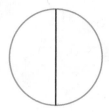
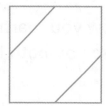
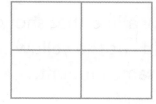
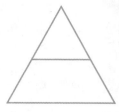

Parts of a Whole

4 Draw two different ways to show fourths.
Shade one fourth of each shape.

Name _____

Describe Equal Parts of a Whole

(I Can) identify, draw, and name equal parts of a whole that is divided in different ways.

Spark Your Learning

Shen, Missy, Aisha, and Zane make flags of the same size with 4 different color sections. Which students divide their flags equally? Which students divide their flags into sections that are not equal?

Zane says his sections are equal in size to Missy's sections. Is he correct? Explain how you know.

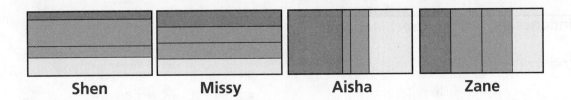

| Shen | Missy | Aisha | Zane |

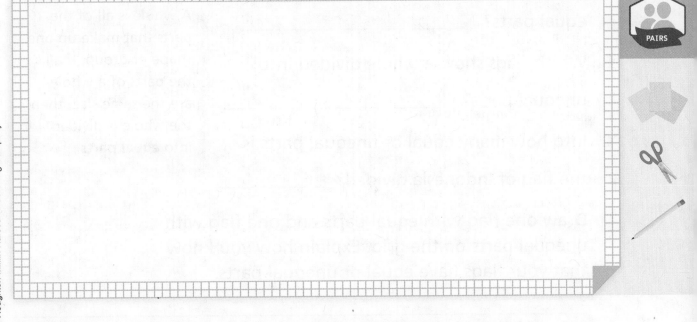

Turn and Talk How can you tell when a shape is divided into equal-sized parts?

Build Understanding

1 Seth compares the flags of different countries.

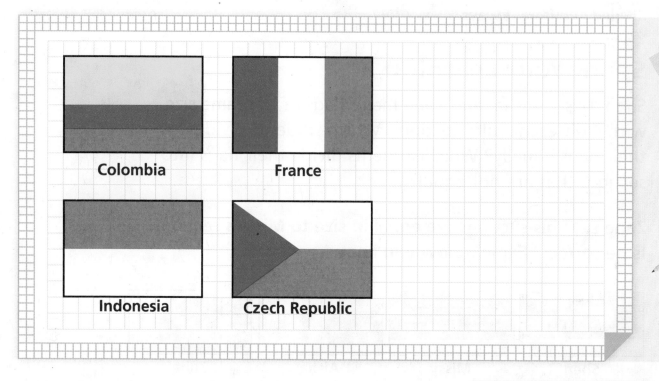

Colombia

France

Indonesia

Czech Republic

A. Which flags show a whole divided into

equal parts? _____

B. Which flags show a whole divided into

unequal parts? _____

C. Into how many equal or unequal parts is

the flag of Indonesia divided? _____

D. Draw one flag with equal parts and one flag with
unequal parts on the grid. Explain how you know
that your flags have equal or unequal parts.

_____

> **Connect to Vocabulary**
>
> A **whole** is all of the
> parts that make up one
> shape or group. If all
> the parts of a whole
> are the same size, then
> the whole is divided
> into **equal parts**.

 Turn and Talk How can you tell when a shape has
been divided into unequal parts?

2 The 137th Street School holds a contest for a new flag design. The school wants all flags to be divided into equal parts.

The name of the equal parts of a whole depends on the total number of equal parts.

Match the flag with the name of the total number of equal parts the whole flag shows.

 • • **thirds**

Think: How do the names of the equal parts relate to the number of equal parts in each flag?

 • • **sixths**

 • • **eighths**

 • • **halves**

 • • **fourths**

 Turn and Talk Do equal parts of a whole need to be the same shape? Explain.

• •

Check Understanding [Math Board]

1 A circle is divided into eighths. How many equal parts does the circle have? _____

2 Is the square divided into thirds? Explain.

_____

_____

On Your Own

Write whether the shape is divided into *equal* parts or *unequal* parts.

3

The parts are

_____.

4

The parts are

_____.

5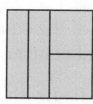

The parts are

_____.

Write the name for the equal parts.

6

_____

7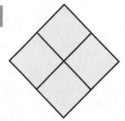

_____

8

_____

9 **STEM** A biologist wants to measure how far bees travel from their hive to obtain nectar. How should the biologist divide this flower field into equal-sized sections? Label the sections 1–6 to record where the bees visit. Explain how you would analyze the results of the experiment.

hive

field

_____

_____

_____

⬡ I'm in a Learning Mindset!

What is still unclear to me about finding equal parts of a whole?

_____

© Houghton Mifflin Harcourt Publishing Company

Name _____

Represent and Name Unit Fractions

(I Can) represent and identify one equal part of a whole or group as a unit fraction.

Spark Your Learning

Mr. Carter has finished building one sixth of his new wooden deck. Draw a picture of what the completed deck might look like.

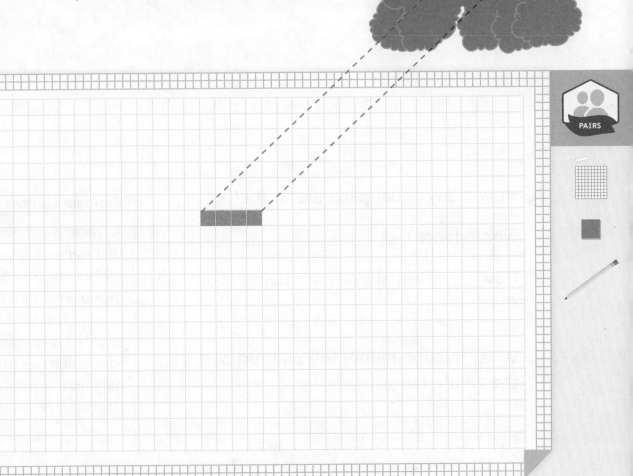

Turn and Talk You know the size and shape of one equal part of a whole. What do you need to know to draw the whole?

Build Understanding

1 Katya is painting a fence. She plans to divide the fence into 4 equal sections.

Katya paints one fourth of the fence. Show how the fence might look after she finishes painting.

A. How many equal parts are in the

whole fence? _____

B. How many equal parts are being counted?

_____

C. What fraction names the painted part of the whole fence?

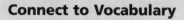

⬜ ←number of equal parts being counted

⬜ ←number of equal parts in the whole

Connect to Vocabulary

A **fraction** is a number that names part of a whole or part of a group. The number of equal parts being counted is compared to the number of equal parts in the whole or in the group. Example:

$$\frac{1}{6}$$

 Turn and Talk What if there are 3 equal sections in a fence and Katya paints 1 section? What fraction could you write to represent the painted section?

2 Lev makes 1 blue T-shirt and 3 yellow T-shirts for the Butterfly Watchers Club. What fraction of the T-shirts is blue?

A. Draw Lev's group of T-shirts.

B. What fraction names the part of the group that is blue?

◄ number of equal parts being counted

◄ number of equal parts in the group

> **Connect to Vocabulary**
>
> A **unit fraction** names 1 equal part of a whole or a group. The number of equal parts counted is 1.
> Example:
> Write: $\frac{1}{8}$
> Read: one eighth

 Turn and Talk Compare the fractions in Task 1 and Task 2. How are they alike? How are they different?

Check Understanding [Math Board]

1 Jess has 5 blue cubes and 1 red cube. What fraction

of the cubes is red? _____

Write a fraction to name the part of the whole or the part of the group that is blue.

2

3

4

_____   _____   _____

On Your Own

5 Tai has 7 red peppers and 1 green pepper. What

fraction of the peppers is green? _____

6 (MP) **Reason** Lara's square is the same size as Kenji's square. Are the two blue parts the same size? Explain.

Lara   Kenji

_____

_____

Write a fraction to name the part of the whole or the part of the group that is blue.

7
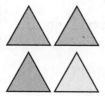

_____

8

_____

9

_____

The shape shows a unit fraction of a whole. Draw to complete the whole shape.

10 a sixth of a shape

$\frac{1}{6}$

11 a third of a shape

$\frac{1}{3}$

12 a half of a shape

$\frac{1}{2}$

⬡ I'm in a Learning Mindset!

With whom should I talk for help in solving problems that involve unit fractions?

_____

Name _____

Represent and Name Fractions of a Whole

(I Can) use a fraction to name an equal part of a whole or an equal part of a group.

Spark Your Learning

Miranda draws a circular design for a playground game. She colors 1 part yellow and 3 parts blue. All of the parts are the same size. What fraction of her game circle is blue?

Show the fraction of Miranda's game circle that is blue.

PAIRS

Turn and Talk What fraction of Miranda's game circle is not blue? How do you know?

Build Understanding

1 May draws a hopscotch game that has 6 equal parts. She uses pink chalk to number the first 2 squares and green chalk to number the rest of the squares. What fraction of the squares have pink numbers?

Show May's hopscotch game.

A. How many equal parts are in the whole? _____

B. How many equal parts are being counted? _____

C. What fraction represents the squares with pink numbers?

> **Connect to Vocabulary**
>
> The **numerator** tells how many parts are being counted. The **denominator** tells how many equal parts are in the whole or in the group.
>
> $\dfrac{3}{6}$ ◄— numerator
> ◄— denominator
>
> Read: three sixths

squares with pink numbers → ⬜ ◄— equal parts being counted
total number of squares → ⬜ ◄— equal parts in the whole

2 For this hopscotch game, the green squares represent what fraction of the whole? Write the fraction.

A. What is the denominator of the fraction? _____

B. What is the numerator of the fraction? _____

C. What is the fraction?

green squares → ⬜ ◄— numerator
total number of squares → ⬜ ◄— denominator

3 Tomi is playing Six Green Marbles. To win the game, Tomi must capture all 6 green marbles.

A. Complete the fractions to show each round of the game.

What fraction of the 6 green marbles does Tomi have:			
after Round 1?	**after Round 2?**	**after Round 3?**	**after Round 4?**
☐/6	☐/6	☐/☐	☐/☐

B. If the pattern continues, what fraction of the 6 green marbles will Tomi have after Round 6? What fraction does this represent? Explain.

_____

_____

 Turn and Talk How are the fractions for each round of Tomi's game related to unit fractions?

• •

Check Understanding [Math Board]

1 The red sections represent what fraction of the playground spinner? Write the fraction in words and numbers.

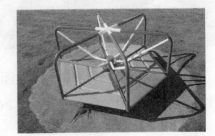

_____ sixths   ☐/☐

On My Own

2 (MP) **Look for Repeated Reasoning** Julie colors four spinners. Complete the fractions to name the part of each spinner that is red.

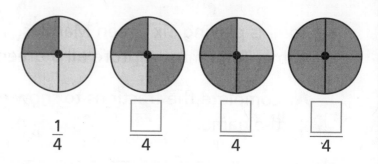

$\dfrac{1}{4}$ $\dfrac{\square}{4}$ $\dfrac{\square}{4}$ $\dfrac{\square}{4}$

- Describe a pattern in the fractions for the spinners.

---

3 Write the fraction that names each equal part. Then write a fraction to name the shaded part of the whole.

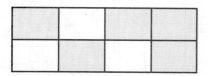

Each equal part is $\dfrac{\square}{\square}$. $\dfrac{\square}{\square}$ is shaded.

4 Shade four of the equal parts. Write the fraction in words and numbers.

 _____ $\dfrac{\square}{\square}$

5 **Cross Curricular Connection:**
Music Each space between the lines on this musical scale identifies a musical note. The four basic notes are shown: F, A, C, and E. Circle each A note. What fraction of the notes on the scale are A notes? Explain.

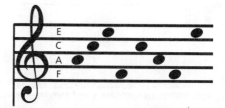

🔢 I'm in a Learning Mindset!

What questions can I ask a classmate that can help me understand how to represent and name fractions?

Name _____

Represent and Name Fractions on a Number Line

(I Can) identify, describe, represent, and locate fractions on a number line.

Spark Your Learning

Michaela works for the Park Service. Her job is to place trail markers on the trail from the Ranger Station to Baldy Mountain. The markers should be placed at locations that mark $\frac{1}{4}$, $\frac{2}{4}$, $\frac{3}{4}$, and $\frac{4}{4}$ of the distance from the Ranger Station to Baldy Mountain.

Show each of Michaela's markers on the number line. Label the distance of each marker from the Ranger Station.

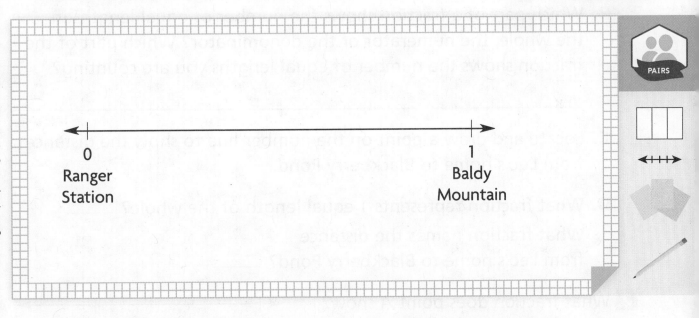

 Turn and Talk Trace the number line on a sheet of paper and fold the paper to show the trail marker locations. How do the folds on your paper number line compare to the labels on your drawing?

Build Understanding

1 On the way to school, Leo stops at Blackberry Pond. What fraction of the 1-mile distance to school has Leo gone?

Complete the fractions on the number line.

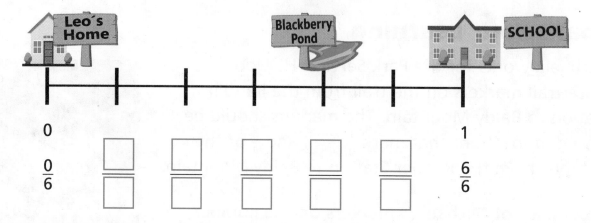

$\frac{0}{6}$　☐/☐　☐/☐　☐/☐　☐/☐　☐/☐　$\frac{6}{6}$

A. Into how many equal lengths is the whole mile divided? _____

B. Which part of a fraction shows the number of equal lengths in the whole, the numerator or the denominator? Which part of the fraction shows the number of equal lengths you are counting?

_____

C. Locate and draw a point on the number line to show the distance from Leo's home to Blackberry Pond.

D. What fraction represents 1 equal length of the whole? _____
What fraction names the distance
from Leo's home to Blackberry Pond? _____

2 What fraction does point *A* show?

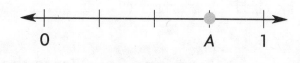

A. Into how many equal lengths is the distance from 0 to 1 divided? _____

B. How many equal lengths are being counted? _____

C. What is the fraction? _____

3 Enya and Kat walk from home to the local history museum. When they are $\frac{1}{3}$ of the way to the museum, they stop at the library. They stop again to read their library books at the park when they are $\frac{2}{3}$ of the way to the museum. Complete the number line to show how to represent these distances.

0   1

Turn and Talk On a number line, what does the length between each whole number represent? What does the length between each mark represent? How do you know?

Check Understanding

1 Complete the number line. Label the fractions. Locate and draw a point on the number line to show $\frac{5}{8}$.

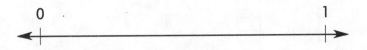

0   1

$\frac{0}{8}$ $\frac{}{8}$ $\frac{}{8}$ ___   ___   ___   ___   ___   ___

Write the fractions that name points E and F.

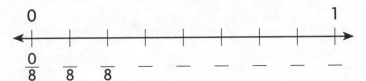

0   1

$\frac{0}{6}$ $\frac{1}{6}$ $\frac{2}{6}$ E   F $\frac{5}{6}$ $\frac{6}{6}$

2 point E ⬚/⬚

3 point F ⬚/⬚

On Your Own

4 (MP) **Use Tools** Reese's poster is $\frac{2}{4}$ yard wide. Complete the number line. Label the fractions. Locate and draw a point on the number line to show the width of Reese's poster.

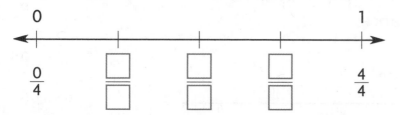

$\frac{0}{4}$ ☐/☐ ☐/☐ ☐/☐ $\frac{4}{4}$

5 Abe marks points *H* and *I* on the number line. Write the fraction that names each point.

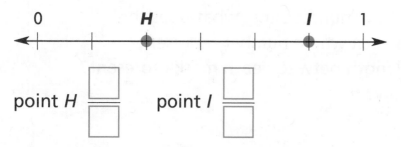

point *H* ☐/☐   point *I* ☐/☐

6 (MP) **Reason** Izzy marks a number line to show eighths. What is the fraction that is located halfway between $\frac{6}{8}$ and $\frac{8}{8}$? Explain.

_____

_____

_____

I'm in a Learning Mindset!

Would drawing my own diagrams help me better understand how to place fractions on a number line?

_____

Express Whole Numbers as Fractions

(I Can) draw visual models to show how to write fractions that name whole numbers.

Spark Your Learning

Mrs. Snow's class has 8 bags of flour. Each bag weighs $\frac{1}{4}$ pound.

Show how many 1-pound sacks of flour the class can fill.

Turn and Talk How can you write the answer to the problem as a fraction?

Build Understanding

1 Tristan makes circular pans of cornbread and cuts them into thirds.

    A. How can you show 1 pan of Tristan's cornbread cut into thirds? How can you show 2 pans cut into thirds?

    B. How many thirds are in two pans? _____

    How can you write this amount as a fraction?

$$\frac{\Box}{\Box}$$

    C. What whole number does the fraction equal?

$$\frac{\Box}{3} = \underline{\quad}$$

2 How can you name the points located on the number line using fractions and whole numbers?

Complete the number line to name the points.

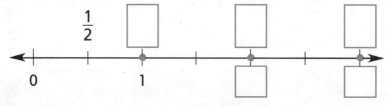

    A. How many equal lengths are there from 0 to 1?

    _____

    B. What whole number and fraction represents 4 equal lengths? _____

    C. What whole number and fraction represents 6 equal lengths? _____

3 Tim uses 4 tortilla halves to make tortilla chips.
Rita uses 9 thirds to make her tortilla chips.
How many whole tortillas do they each use?

Draw to show each fraction.

A. What fractions represent Tim's chips and Rita's
chips? How many whole tortillas does each fraction
represent?

Tim: $\dfrac{\boxed{}}{\boxed{}}$ = _____ wholes   Rita: $\dfrac{\boxed{}}{\boxed{}}$ = _____ wholes

B. How many whole tortillas do they each use?

_____

_____

 Turn and Talk Without drawing a picture, what
strategy can you use to write $\frac{18}{6}$ as a whole number?

• •

Check Understanding

1 Each circle is 1 whole. Write a whole number
and a fraction for the parts that are shaded.

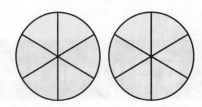

_____ = $\dfrac{\boxed{}}{6}$

On Your Own

2 (MP) **Use Tools** Peter uses 8 one-half fraction circle pieces to make whole circles. Show the whole circles that Peter makes.

Peter makes _____ whole circles.

3 Circle the fraction on the number line that is the same as 1 whole. Draw a box around the fraction that is the same as 2 wholes.

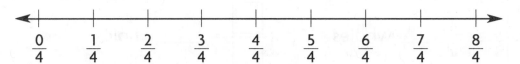

Each square is 1 whole. Write a whole number and a fraction for the parts that are shaded.

6 (MP) **Reason** Belle runs 16 times around a track that measures $\frac{1}{4}$ mile long. Write a fraction that shows the distance that Belle runs. How many whole

miles does Belle run? _____

⬡ I'm in a Learning Mindset!

How is solving fraction problems different when I work with a partner?

_____

Name _____

Represent and Name Fractions Greater Than 1

(I Can) identify fractions greater than 1 on a number line and write them in fraction form and as mixed numbers.

Spark Your Learning

Emilio cuts his pizzas into slices. Each slice is a fourth of a whole pizza. Emilio has 9 slices to sell.

Emilio's Pizza

Special: $\frac{1}{4}$ of a pizza
Now Available

Show all the different amounts of pizza that Emilio can sell. Name each fraction that you show.

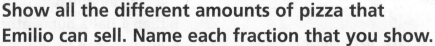

SMALL GROUPS

 Turn and Talk The numerator of a fraction is greater than the denominator. What does that tell you about the fraction?

Build Understanding

1 Jasmine has a stack of 7 waffle halves. How many plates can Jasmine fill with 1 whole waffle? Will any waffle halves be left over?

Draw to show the waffles.

$\frac{1}{2}$ of a waffle

A. How many plates does Jasmine fill with whole waffles? _____

B. How many halves are left over? _____

C. What fraction greater than 1 and mixed number can you write to represent the waffles that Jasmine serves?

____ = ____ wholes + ____ left over = ____

2 To make a shirt, Luc needs $\frac{5}{3}$ yards of cloth.

Complete the number line to show thirds.

A. How many thirds are in 1 yard? _____

B. How many whole yards does Luc need? Circle the fraction on the number line that shows this. _____

C. Circle the section of the number line which represents the amount that Luc still needs.

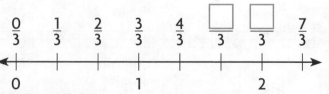

D. Write a mixed number to represent $\frac{5}{3}$.

whole yards _____ fraction of a whole yard

3 Nisa's egg cartons each hold 8 eggs. Nisa has 17 eggs. How many cartons of eggs does Nisa fill?

A. Draw to show the eggs in Nisa's cartons.

1 carton = 1 whole

B. How many whole cartons does Nisa

fill completely? _____

C. How many eggs are left over? What fraction of a

carton is left over? _____

D. Write the number of cartons Nisa fills as a

mixed number. Nisa fills _____ cartons of eggs.

 Turn and Talk How many more eggs does Nisa need to fill her partly-filled carton? Explain how you know.

Check Understanding

1 Shel has $\frac{11}{8}$ pizzas to sell. How much pizza does he have?

Write the mixed number. _____ pizzas

2 Mae swims $\frac{1}{2}$ mile each day. How many miles does Mae swim in 5 days? Complete the number line to show the distance and write the distance as a mixed number.

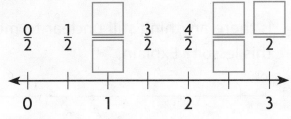

Mae swims _____ miles.

On Your Own

3 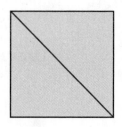 **(MP) Use Repeated Reasoning** The square represents 1 whole and each triangle represents $\frac{1}{2}$ of a whole. How would you represent $3\frac{1}{2}$?

_____

4 **(MP) Use Structure** Jerry has 14 lemons that are packed in bags of 6 lemons. How many bags of lemons does Jerry have? Write a mixed number.

_____

5 Nya needs string that is nine-sixths feet long. Complete the number line to show the length of string that Nya needs.

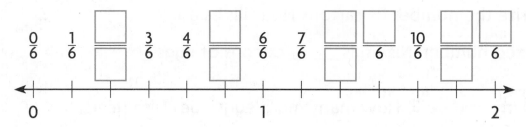

Write a mixed number. Nya needs _____ feet of string.

Write the fraction as a mixed number.

6 $\frac{5}{4}$ **7** $\frac{7}{3}$ **8** $\frac{10}{8}$ **9** $\frac{9}{4}$

_____   _____   _____   _____

⬡ I'm in a Learning Mindset!

Is there anything still unclear to me about mixed numbers after finishing this lesson? Explain.

_____

_____

Name _____

Use Fractions to Measure Lengths

(I Can) measure lengths to the nearest half or fourth of an inch using a ruler.

Spark Your Learning

Sia needs to measure the length of the carrots that she is growing for a science experiment.

About how long is each of Sia's carrots?

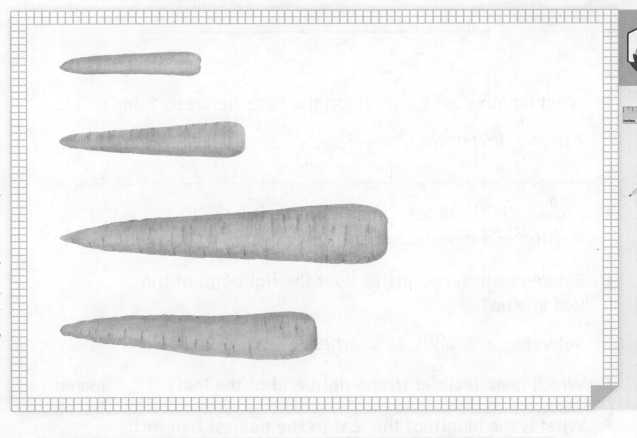

SMALL GROUPS

🗣 **Turn and Talk** How did you decide on a measurement when the length of the carrot was between two markings on the ruler?

Build Understanding

1 Measure the length of a leaf. Use a ruler marked with half inches.

A. Line up the left end of the leaf with the zero mark on the ruler.

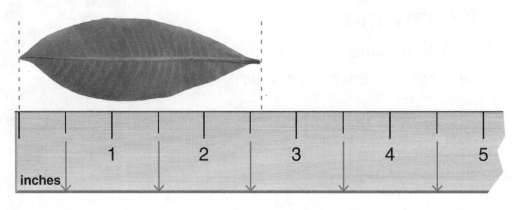

_____ _____ _____ _____ _____

B. What length does the mark on the ruler between 1 and 2 show? How do you know? _____

_____

C. Label each of the other marks on the ruler with a fraction or a mixed number.

D. Between which two marks does the right end of the leaf line up?

Between _____ and _____ inches

E. Which mark is closer to the right end of the leaf? _____ inches

F. What is the length of the leaf to the nearest half inch?

_____ inches

 Turn and Talk How is a ruler like a number line? Explain.

Name _____

Step It Out

2 Measure the length of this carrot to the nearest fourth, or quarter inch.

A. Line up the left end of the carrot with the zero mark on the ruler.

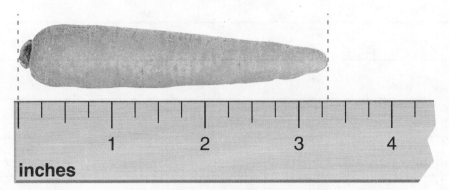

inches

B. The right end of the carrot is between

_____ and _____ inches.

C. Which fourth-inch mark is closer to the right

end of the carrot? _____-inch mark

D. The length of the carrot to the nearest

fourth inch is _____ inches.

 Turn and Talk Where is the zero mark on the ruler? How do you know?

A ruler showing fourths is like a number line that is divided into fourths.

$$\frac{0}{4} \quad \frac{1}{4} \quad \frac{2}{4} \quad \frac{3}{4} \quad \frac{4}{4}$$

↓ ↓ ↓ ↓ ↓

1

inches

↓ ↓ ↓ ↓ ↓

0   1

....

Check Understanding [Math Board]

Use a ruler marked with half inches. Measure.

1 What is the length of the stick to the nearest half inch?

_____

© Houghton Mifflin Harcourt Publishing Company • Image Credit: ©Napat/Shutterstock

On Your Own

2 (MP) **Critique Reasoning** Alma and Rex both measure the same pen. Alma says the pen is about $5\frac{1}{2}$ inches long. Rex says the pen is about $5\frac{1}{4}$ inches long. Can both students be correct? Explain.

_____

_____

_____

_____

Use a ruler marked with fourth inches for 3–5. Measure.

3 What is the length of the nut to the nearest fourth inch?

_____

4 What is the length of the safety pin to the nearest half inch?

_____

5 Draw a line that is $4\frac{3}{4}$ inches in length.

⬡ I'm in a Learning Mindset!

How does using a ruler help me better understand measuring with fractions?

_____

_____

Module 13 Review

Vocabulary

1 Write each number under the category that it matches.

$\frac{1}{2}$ 4 $1\frac{1}{3}$ $\frac{11}{8}$ $\frac{1}{4}$ $\frac{5}{4}$ 2 $3\frac{1}{2}$ $\frac{1}{8}$

fraction greater than 1	mixed number	unit fraction	whole number

Concepts and Skills

2 Draw lines to divide the shape into eighths.

Shade 1 part of the shape. Write the fraction that names the shaded part.

3 (MP) **Use Tools** Each triangle represents $\frac{1}{2}$ of a whole square. How many triangles do you need to make $\frac{7}{2}$? Tell what strategy or tool you will use to solve the problem, explain your choice, and then find the answer.

(A) 6   (C) 8

(B) 7   (D) 14

4 Which fraction names the shaded part?

Ⓐ $\frac{1}{4}$　　　Ⓑ $\frac{1}{6}$　　　Ⓒ $\frac{5}{6}$　　　Ⓓ $\frac{6}{6}$

5 Which fraction is represented by the point on the number line?

Ⓐ $\frac{1}{1}$　　　Ⓑ $\frac{1}{2}$　　　Ⓒ $\frac{1}{3}$　　　Ⓓ $\frac{1}{4}$

6 Which number line shows $\frac{3}{3}$?

Ⓐ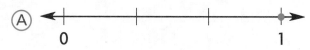

Ⓑ

Ⓒ

Ⓓ

7 Which is the length of the craft stick to the nearest half inch?

Ⓐ 4 inches　　　Ⓒ 5 inches

Ⓑ $4\frac{1}{2}$ inches　　　Ⓓ $5\frac{1}{2}$ inches

Relate Shapes, Fractions, and Area

How can I show half?

- Draw an outline around half of the rectangle. Describe your outline.

_____

- Make a pattern inside the rectangle by shading squares. Shade exactly half of the whole rectangle.

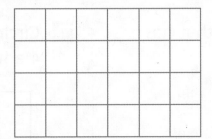

- Count the number of squares you shaded.

_____

 Turn and Talk

- Compare your pattern with your those of your classmates. What is similar and different about the patterns?

- How can you find the number of shaded squares in the rectangle without counting each one?

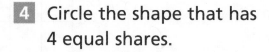
Are You Ready?

Complete these problems to review prior concepts and skills you will need for this module.

Partition Shapes

1 Draw lines to show fourths. Shade one fourth of the shape.

2 Draw lines to show halves. Shade one half of the shape.

Equal Shares

3 Circle the shape that has 2 equal shares.

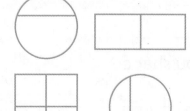

4 Circle the shape that has 4 equal shares.

Fractions of a Whole

Write the number of equal parts in the whole. Then write the fraction that names the shaded part.

5

_____ equal parts

_____

6

_____ equal parts

_____

7

_____ equal parts

_____

Name _____

Relate Fractions and Area

(I Can) use a fraction to show that equal parts of a whole shape have the same area.

Spark Your Learning

Liddy's hamsters are Alvin, Betty, Coco, and Doug. Liddy puts up a wall to divide her hamsters' playground into left and right halves. Then she puts up screens to divide each half of the playground into two halves. Now each hamster has a separate play space.

Which hamster will get the largest play space? Explain your thinking.

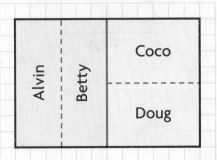

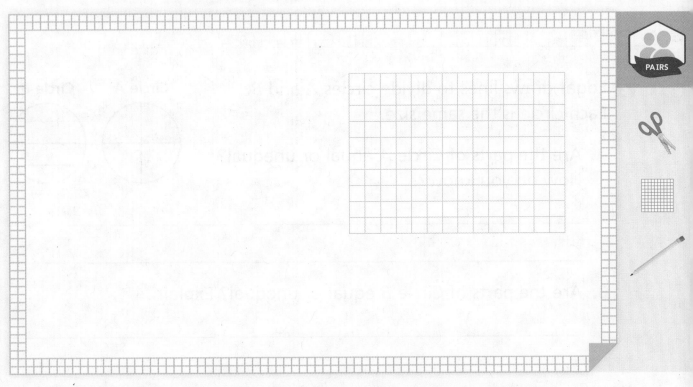

Turn and Talk What fraction of the whole playground does each hamster's play space represent? How do you know?

Build Understanding

1 Davita draws lines to divide shapes *A*, *B*, and *C*. Which shapes are divided into equal areas?

How can you show which shapes are divided into equal areas?

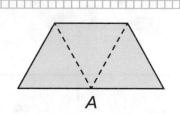 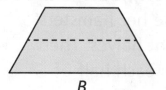 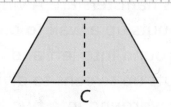

2 Edgar draws lines to divide circles *A* and *B*.
Each circle is the same size.

Circle *A*   Circle *B*

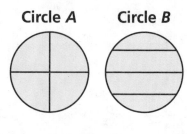

A. Are the parts of Circle *A* equal or unequal?
How do you know?

_____

_____

B. Are the parts of Circle *B* equal or unequal? Explain.

_____

_____

 Turn and Talk When two areas appear to be the same size, how can you show that they are actually equal?

3 Reyna divides a rectangle into parts.

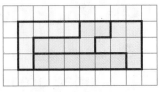

A. Are the parts of the rectangle the same shape? Explain how you know.

_____

_____

B. Do the parts of the rectangle have the same area? How do you know?

_____

_____

C. What fraction of the total area of the rectangle is shaded yellow? How do you know?

_____

_____

Turn and Talk A sign painter paints two signs with different shapes. Sign *A* is a triangle and sign *B* is a rectangle. How is it possible that both signs require the same amount of paint? Explain.

• •

Check Understanding

1 Circle the shape that is divided into parts with equal areas.

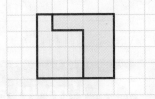

2 For the rectangle shown:

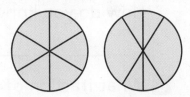

• Do both parts of this rectangle have the same shape? Explain how you know.

_____

_____

• Which part of the rectangle covers a greater area? How do you know?

_____

On Your Own

3 **(MP)** **Critique Reasoning** Garrick says that the shaded area is $\frac{1}{3}$ of the whole because it is 1 of 3 parts that all have the same shape. Aidan says that the shaded area is not $\frac{1}{3}$ of the whole because the three parts do not all have the same area. Which student's reasoning is correct? Explain.

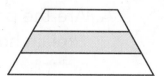

_____

_____

4 Cross out any shapes that have parts with unequal areas.

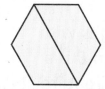   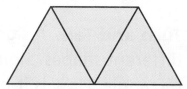

Use the rectangle for 5–6.

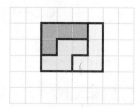

5 Are the parts of the rectangle equal in area? How do you know?

_____

6 What fraction of the rectangle is shaded blue?

_____

➗ I'm in a Learning Mindset!

What do I already know about dividing shapes that will help me find whether a shape is divided into equal areas?

_____

_____

Name

Partition Shapes into Equal Areas

(I Can) divide shapes into parts with equal areas and write each equal part as a fraction.

Spark Your Learning

Mia designs a playground. She plans to divide it into 4 parts with equal areas. So far, Mia has found one way to divide the playground.

Show another way to divide the playground. Explain how you know that the 4 parts of your plan are equal in area.

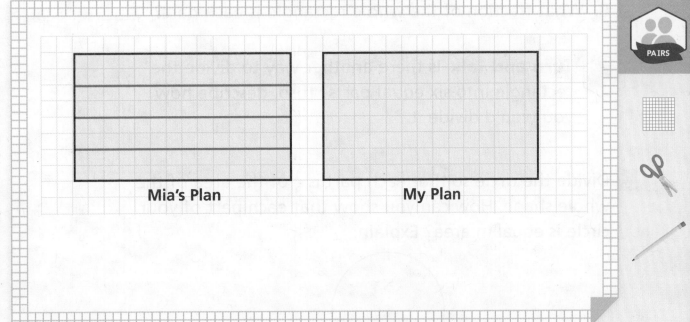

Mia's Plan   My Plan

PAIRS

Turn and Talk Can two rectangles be equal in area if they have different shapes? How do you know?

Build Understanding

1 How can you divide the rectangle into 6 parts with equal areas?

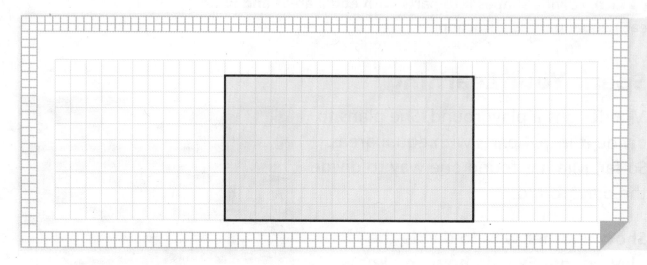

A. How do you know that the parts are equal in area?

_____

B. What fraction of the whole rectangle is each part? _____

 Turn and Talk Is there another way to divide the rectangle into six equal parts? If so, describe how you would divide it.

2 Divide the circle so that each part is $\frac{1}{3}$ of the area of the whole shape. How can you show that each part of your circle is equal in area? Explain.

_____

_____

3  **Critique Reasoning** Angela and Pedro divide rectangles into 8 equal parts in different ways. Both rectangles are the same size and shape.

Angela's Way   Pedro's Way

A. Do the parts from Angela's rectangle have the same shape as the parts from Pedro's rectangle? Explain.

_____

_____

B. Who divided the rectangle into parts that are greater in area, Angela or Pedro? Explain how you know.

_____

_____

Turn and Talk How can you show another way to divide the rectangle into 8 equal parts?

Check Understanding [Math Board]

1 What fraction of the total area of the circle does each

equal part represent? _____

2 Nora and Nick cut felt squares to make 6 equal-sized patches. Nick wants his patches to have a different shape but the same area as Nora's patches. Draw lines to show how they can cut each of the felt squares.

Nora   Nick

On Your Own

3 (MP) **Construct Arguments** Glenn says he can divide the six-sided shape into 3 parts with equal areas. Emily says she can divide the shape into 6 parts with equal areas. Whose statement is correct? Draw to explain.

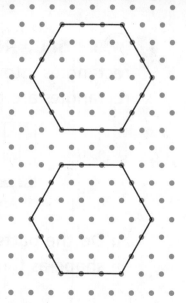

_____

_____

_____

4 (MP) **Attend to Precision** Divide the shape into 6 equal parts.

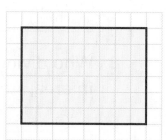

- How do you know that you divided your shape into 6 equal parts?

_____

_____

Use the shapes for 5–6.

5 Shade $\frac{1}{4}$ of the shape on the left.

6 Is there another way to divide the shape into 4 equal parts? _____

If yes, draw lines on the shape on the right to show a way. Shade the shape to show $\frac{1}{4}$.

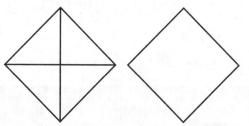

⊹ I'm in a Learning Mindset!

How can I use different tools and strategies to help me see if I have divided a shape into parts with equal areas?

_____

Name

Use Unit Fractions to Describe Area

(I Can) write a unit fraction to represent the area of each equal part of a whole shape.

Spark Your Learning

Rex plans to divide the hexagonal-shaped pool into 6 equal parts and paint 1 part green. What unit fraction of the pool should Rex paint?

Show how Rex should divide the pool. Name the unit fraction of the pool that he should paint. Explain your thinking.

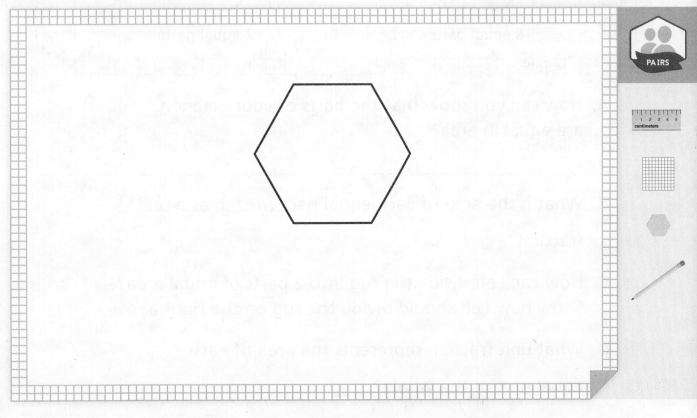

PAIRS

 Turn and Talk Describe two ways in which Rex can paint one half of the pool pink.

© Houghton Mifflin Harcourt Publishing Company

Build Understanding

1 Leif is designing an octagonal-shaped rug. He wants to divide the rug into 8 parts that each have an equal area. How can you write the area of each part as a unit fraction of the whole?

Show how Leif should divide the rug on the left.

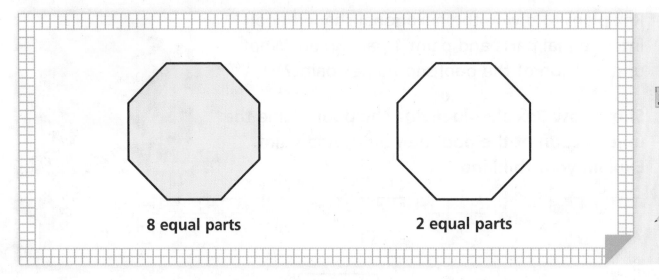

8 equal parts   2 equal parts

A. How can you show that the parts of your octagon are equal in area?

_____

B. What is the area of each equal part written as a unit

   fraction? _____

C. How can Leif divide the rug into 2 parts of equal area? Show how Leif should divide the rug on the right above.

D. What unit fraction represents the area of each

   equal part of the whole? _____

 Turn and Talk Can you think of another way to divide the rug into 2 equal parts? Explain.

Step It Out

2 ▸ Meg divides a circular-shaped rug into equal parts. How can you write the area of each part of Meg's rug as a unit fraction?

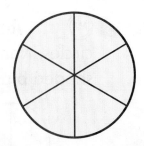

A. Find the denominator. How many equal parts are in the whole?

_____ equal parts in the whole

B. Find the numerator. How many parts are being counted?

_____ part counted

C. The area of each equal part of Meg's rug is $\dfrac{\square}{\square}$.

 Turn and Talk Meg divides another identical rug into four equal parts. Will each equal part be larger or smaller in area than the parts in the diagram above? Explain.

• •

Check Understanding

1 Divide the shape into 2 equal areas. What unit fraction names each equal part of the shape?

$\dfrac{\square}{\square}$

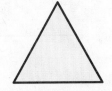

2 Divide the shape into 3 equal areas. What unit fraction names each equal part of the shape?

$\dfrac{\square}{\square}$

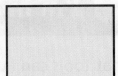

On Your Own

3 **(MP)** **Use Repeated Reasoning** Ina shades four fraction circles. Name the unit fraction that matches the area shaded blue.

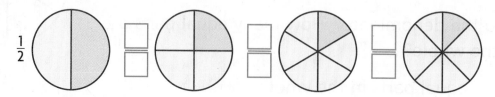

$\frac{1}{2}$

- Describe a pattern you see in the fractions.

_____

4 **(MP)** **Critique Reasoning** Kimo says he colored $\frac{1}{6}$ of the square green. Is Kimo correct? Explain.

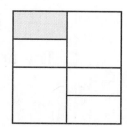

_____

_____

5 **STEM** Computer engineers use real batting record data to design this computer baseball game.

- What fraction of the game board counts for a double? _____

- Which is more likely, that a player gets a home run or a strike out?

_____

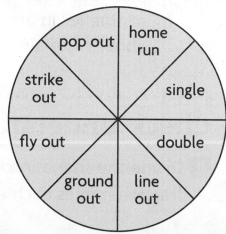

🔷 I'm in a Learning Mindset!

What tools can I use to check to see if I can write the area of each part of a shape as a unit fraction of a whole?

_____

Module 14 Review

Vocabulary

Choose the correct term from the Vocabulary box.

1 Each equal part that a whole is divided into

is a _____.

2 The number of unit squares needed to cover

a surface is the _____.

3 A square with a side length of 1 unit is called a

_____.

Concepts and Skills

4 Divide the shape into 2 equal areas.

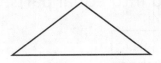

What unit fraction names each equal part of the shape? _____

5 (MP) **Use Tools** Martha colored 1 of 8 parts of the shape. She says she colored $\frac{1}{8}$ of the shape. Is Martha correct? Explain. Tell what strategy or tool you will use to solve the problem, explain your choice, and then find the answer.

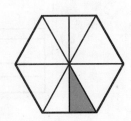

_____

_____

_____

6 Divide the shape into 4 parts that each have an equal area.

7 Which unit fraction of the circular shape does each equal part represent?

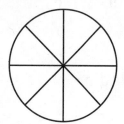

(A) $\frac{1}{3}$

(C) $\frac{1}{6}$

(B) $\frac{1}{4}$

(D) $\frac{1}{8}$

8 Select all of the shapes that are divided into equal parts.

(A)

(D)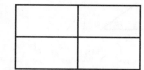

(B)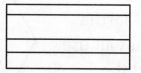

(E)

(C)

Compare Fractions

What fraction of the target is red?

James and Kira play a bean-bag-toss game. The target has four sections. Each section of the target starts as blue. When hit with a bean bag, the section flips to its red side. The goal is to flip all sections to red.

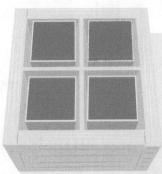

A player tosses 4 bean bags in each round. Below are the results for two rounds.

Round 1

James   Kira

Round 2

James   Kira

- For Round 1, what fraction names the red part of the target for the two players? for Round 2?

 Turn and Talk

- How can you describe how close each player is to the goal at the end of Round 2?

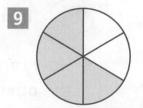

Are You Ready?

Complete these problems to review prior concepts and skills you will need for this module.

Compare Numbers

Compare the numbers. Write <, >, or =.

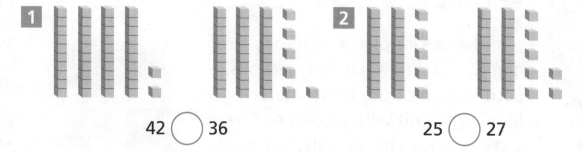

1 42 ◯ 36

2 25 ◯ 27

Locate Numbers on a Number Line

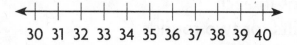

30 31 32 33 34 35 36 37 38 39 40

3 What number is just after 34? _____

4 What number is just before 32? _____

5 What number is between 37 and 39? _____

6 Mark each number on the number line.

Fractions of a Whole

Write the fraction that names the shaded part of the whole.

7

8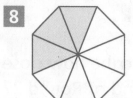

9

_____   _____   _____

Name

Compare Fractions Using Concrete and Visual Models

(I Can) use concrete and visual models to compare fractions.

Spark Your Learning

Rafael and Frankie each paint 4 equal parts of their doghouse walls. Each wall is the same size. Who uses more paint?

Show one way to find who uses more paint.

Rafael's
Doghouse

Frankie's
Doghouse

Rafael's Wall

Frankie's Wall

PAIRS

$\frac{1}{2}$

Turn and Talk Toby paints 4 of 6 sections on a small doghouse wall. Nan paints 4 of 6 sections on a large doghouse wall. Toby says that he and Nan used the same amount of paint because $\frac{4}{6} = \frac{4}{6}$. Does Toby's statement make sense? Why or why not?

Build Understanding

South Rink

1 The Jasper City Parks Department marks off $\frac{3}{4}$ of its South Rink for Family Skating. In the North Rink, $\frac{3}{8}$ of the space is used for Family Skating. Both rinks are the same size and shape.

North Rink

Use a concrete or visual model to show and compare the parts of the rinks that are used for Family Skating.

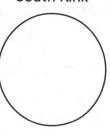

South Rink   North Rink

A. Which rink has a larger area for Family Skating? How do you know?

_____

_____

_____

B. Compare the fractions. $\frac{3}{4} \bigcirc \frac{3}{8}$

2 Use the visual model to compare $\frac{4}{8}$ and $\frac{5}{8}$.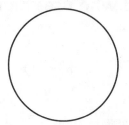

A. Shade to show $\frac{4}{8}$ and $\frac{5}{8}$. Which fraction has the larger amount of the whole shaded? How do you know?

_____

B. Write <, >, or =. $\frac{4}{8} \bigcirc \frac{5}{8}$

3 Emily climbs $\frac{2}{8}$ of the way up the climbing wall. Ryan climbs $\frac{2}{3}$ of the way up the wall.

A. Show how you can compare the fractions on the number lines. Label the distances.

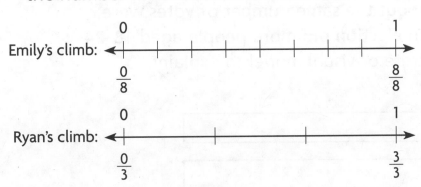

Emily's climb:

$\frac{0}{8}$ $\frac{8}{8}$

Ryan's climb:

$\frac{0}{3}$ $\frac{3}{3}$

B. Write <, >, or =. $\frac{2}{8}$ ◯ $\frac{2}{3}$

C. Who climbs higher? How do you know?

Turn and Talk How can the size of the equal lengths in the whole help you find which fraction is greater?

Check Understanding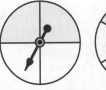

1 Which spinner has a larger area shaded?

Write the fractions. Write <, >, or =.

Shade to show each fraction. Write <, >, or =.

2 Compare $\frac{4}{8}$ and $\frac{4}{6}$.

$\frac{4}{8}$ ◯ $\frac{4}{6}$

3 Compare $\frac{4}{6}$ and $\frac{2}{6}$.

$\frac{4}{6}$ ◯ $\frac{2}{6}$

On Your Own

4 **Social Studies** Tim compared total votes for voters aged 18–24. In a 2016 election, $\frac{2}{8}$ of people aged 18–24 voted. In 2018, $\frac{2}{6}$ of the same age group voted. In both elections, about the same number of votes were counted. In which election did more people aged 18–24 vote? Use a concrete or visual model to explain your answer.

2016:

2018:

5 **(MP) Attend to Precision** Patty walks $\frac{2}{4}$ mile on Monday and $\frac{3}{4}$ miie on Tuesday. Show the distances on the number line. On which day does Patty walk a shorter distance? How do you know?

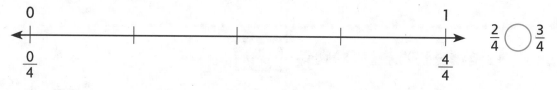

$$\frac{2}{4} \bigcirc \frac{3}{4}$$

⊹ I'm in a Learning Mindset!

How can I share the visual or concrete models I used to compare fractions to help other students with their fraction comparisons?

Name _____

Compare Fractions with the Same Denominator

(I Can) compare fractions that are divided into an equal number of same-sized parts.

Spark Your Learning

Ulan and Hector both like to read. Ulan has finished $\frac{3}{8}$ of her book. Hector has finished $\frac{5}{8}$ of the same book. Who has read more of the book?

Show how you can tell who has read more of the book.

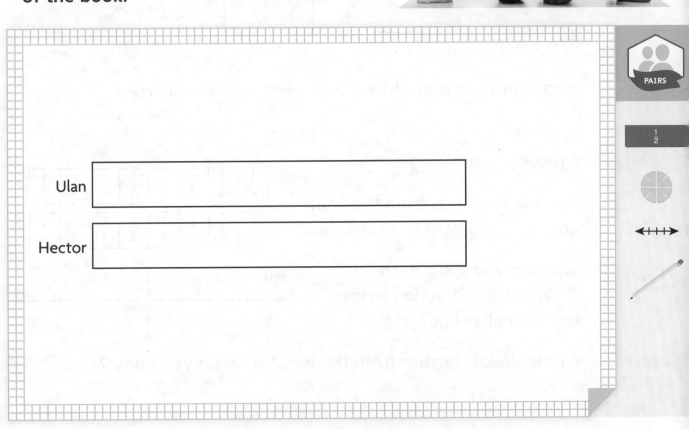

Ulan

Hector

PAIRS

$\frac{1}{2}$

 Turn and Talk Jory has finished $\frac{4}{8}$ of the same book. How does her reading compare with that of Ulan and of Hector?

Build Understanding

1 Both Rennie and Leah paint same-sized patios that are divided into 6 equal sections. Rennie paints $\frac{3}{6}$ of his patio floor orange. Leah paints $\frac{4}{6}$ of her patio floor pink. Who paints less area?

A. How can you represent the areas that Rennie and Leah paint?.

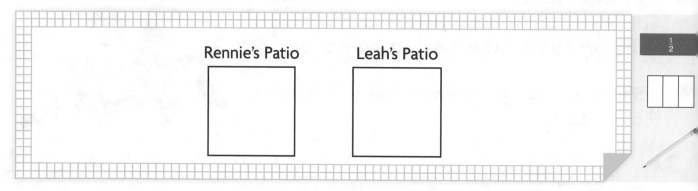

Rennie's Patio   Leah's Patio

B. Who paints less area of the patio? How do you know?

_____

C. Write <, >, or =. $\frac{3}{6} \bigcirc \frac{4}{6}$

2 Ellen's desk is $\frac{7}{4}$ yards from the wall. Ethan's desk is $\frac{3}{4}$ yard from the wall.

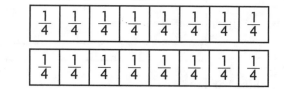
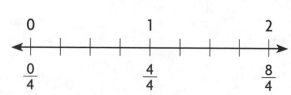

A. How can you show each distance using fraction strips and a number line?

B. Whose desk is farther from the wall? How do you know?

$\frac{7}{4} \bigcirc \frac{3}{4}$ _____

 Turn and Talk What is a quick way to find out which fraction is greater if both fractions have the same denominator?

Step It Out

3 Len uses $\frac{5}{8}$ of a wooden board to make a roof for a tree house. Raylette uses $\frac{7}{8}$ of a same-sized board to make a chair. Who uses more of their board? Show where Len and Raylette cut their boards.

A. When equal-sized wholes are divided into the same number of equal parts, the denominators are the same. You can then look at the _____ to compare the number of parts being counted.

B. Each whole board has _____ equal parts.

Compare the numerators. _____ parts are more than

_____ parts. _____ > _____, so .

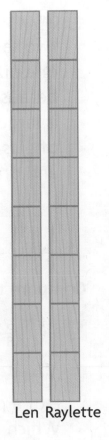
Len Raylette

C. Who uses more of their board? _____

D. To compare fractions with the same denominator, how do the numerators tell you which fraction is greater?

_____

Turn and Talk Use a visual model to justify how you made your comparisons.

• •

Check Understanding [Math Board]

1 On Tuesday, it rains $\frac{3}{4}$ inch. On Wednesday, it rains $\frac{2}{4}$ inch. On which day is there more rain? Draw a visual model to

justify your answer. _____

On Your Own

2 (MP) **Construct Arguments** Lisa has two same-sized pizzas. She says $\frac{3}{8}$ of one pizza is greater than $\frac{5}{8}$ of the other because each of the 3 equal parts in $\frac{3}{8}$ is larger than each of the 5 equal parts of $\frac{5}{8}$. Is Lisa correct? Explain your answer and draw a visual model to show your reasoning.

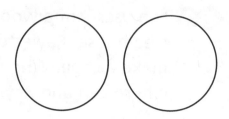

_____

_____

Compare the fractions. Write <, >, or =.

3 $\frac{3}{8} \bigcirc \frac{5}{8}$

4 $\frac{5}{6} \bigcirc \frac{4}{6}$

5 $\frac{5}{3} \bigcirc \frac{5}{3}$

6 (MP) **Reason** Remi's family eats $\frac{2}{6}$ of a carrot loaf and $\frac{3}{6}$ of a pumpkin loaf. Both loaves are the same size. Which loaf has less left over? Explain.

_____

_____

_____

➕✖➗ I'm in a Learning Mindset!

How can I take notes to help me if I get confused about comparing fractions that have the same denominator?

_____

Name _____

Compare Fractions with the Same Numerator

(I Can) compare fractions that count the same number of equal parts when the whole is divided into a different number of equal parts.

Spark Your Learning

Nita and Bennet are riding in the Around-the-Park Bike Ride. Nita completes $\frac{3}{4}$ of the ride. Bennet completes $\frac{3}{6}$ of the ride. Who rides farther?

Show one way to compare the distances.

Nita

Bennet

Turn and Talk What is the same about both fractions? How does this help you find out which fraction is greater?

Build Understanding

1 Elan and Tanya both plan to film one-minute videos. So far, Elan has filmed $\frac{2}{6}$ of his video. Tanya has filmed $\frac{2}{3}$ of her video. Who has filmed less, so far?

A. Show one way to solve the problem.

Elan

Tanya

B. Write <, >, or = to compare the fractions. $\frac{2}{6}$ ◯ $\frac{2}{3}$

C. Who films less of the video? How do you know?

_____

2 Rocky hikes $\frac{5}{6}$ of the Pino Trail. Rini hikes $\frac{5}{8}$ of the trail. Who hikes a greater distance on the trail?

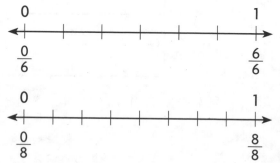

A. How can you show the distances on the number lines? Which fraction is closer to 1? _____

B. Write <, >, or = to compare the fractions. $\frac{5}{6}$ ◯ $\frac{5}{8}$

Who hikes farther? _____

 Turn and Talk How does the number of equal lengths in the whole affect the size of each equal length? How can you use this relationship to compare the fractions in Task 2?

Step It Out

3 Aiden climbs $\frac{2}{9}$ of the way up the rope ladder.
Reid climbs $\frac{2}{5}$ of the way up the same rope ladder.
Who climbs higher?

A. How do the numerators compare? _____

B. How do the denominators compare?

Aiden: The whole is divided into _____ parts.

Reid: The whole is divided into _____ parts.

Whose equal parts are larger in size? How do you know?

_____

_____

C. Are 2 of the equal parts in Reid's climb smaller than or larger than

2 of the equal parts in Aiden's climb? _____

D. Compare the fractions. $\frac{2}{9}$ ◯ $\frac{2}{5}$ Who climbs higher? _____

 Turn and Talk How can you use the size of the
equal parts to find which fraction is greater?

• •

Check Understanding

1 Roxanne paints $\frac{4}{6}$ of a poster red. Max paints $\frac{4}{8}$ of a same-
sized poster red. Who paints more of their poster red?

How do you know? _____

Compare. Write <, >, or =.

2 $\frac{3}{4}$ ◯ $\frac{3}{8}$

3 $\frac{2}{5}$ ◯ $\frac{2}{3}$

4 $\frac{4}{6}$ ◯ $\frac{4}{4}$

On Your Own

5 (MP) **Reason** On a hike, Lilly eats $\frac{2}{3}$ of her granola bar. Pat eats $\frac{2}{4}$ of his bar. Both bars are the same size. Who eats less? Explain your answer.

_____

_____

_____

Compare the fractions. Write <, >, or =.

6 $\frac{3}{4}$ ◯ $\frac{3}{6}$

7 $\frac{4}{8}$ ◯ $\frac{4}{8}$

8 $\frac{5}{3}$ ◯ $\frac{5}{8}$

9 **STEM** Igneous rocks such as feldspar form when different types of melted rock deep inside Earth cool and harden. Igneous rock sample A is $\frac{3}{8}$ feldspar. Igneous rock sample B is $\frac{3}{5}$ feldspar. Both rocks weigh the same. Which rock has a greater amount of feldspar? Explain.

sample A
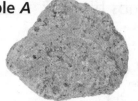

sample B

_____

_____

_____

⬡ I'm in a Learning Mindset!

What do I already know about numerators and denominators that will help me compare fractions that have the same numerator?

_____

Name _____

Use Reasoning Strategies to Compare Fractions

(I Can) use different reasoning strategies to compare fractions.

Spark Your Learning

Nora picks $\frac{3}{4}$ pound of cherries. Ned picks $\frac{7}{8}$ pound of cherries. Who picks the greater amount of cherries?

Show your strategy for comparing the fractions.

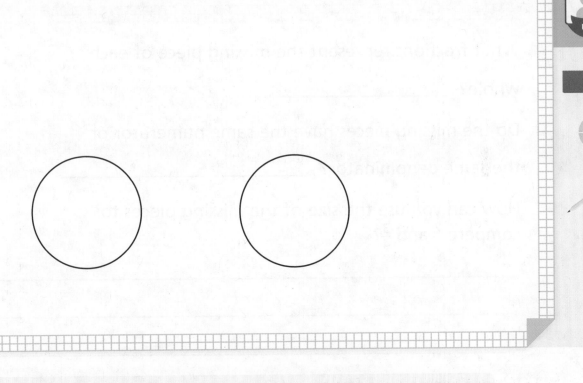

Turn and Talk What do you notice about the size of the missing piece in each of the fractions you compared? How can you use the missing piece and reasoning to compare the fractions?

Build Understanding

1 Ian's granola bar recipe calls for $\frac{2}{3}$ cup of oats. Sadie's recipe uses $\frac{3}{4}$ cup of oats. Whose recipe uses fewer oats?

Show how to compare $\frac{2}{3}$ and $\frac{3}{4}$.

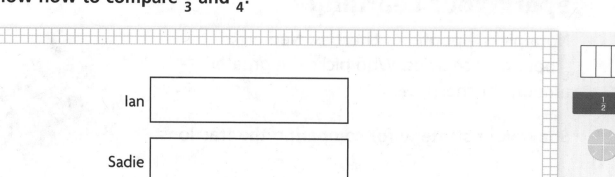

A. What fractions represent the missing piece of each whole? _____

B. Do the missing pieces have the same numerator or the same denominator? _____

C. How can you use the size of the missing pieces to compare $\frac{2}{3}$ and $\frac{3}{4}$?

_____

_____

_____

D. Whose recipe uses fewer oats? _____

 Turn and Talk For you, which is most important for comparing fractions—the numerators, the denominators, or your visual models?

Step It Out

2 ▸ Beth's glass of orange juice is $\frac{3}{8}$ full. Leo's glass is $\frac{3}{4}$ full. Both glasses hold the same amount. Whose glass has more juice? Choose a strategy to compare the fractions.

Same Denominator:	Same Numerator:	Missing Pieces:
The fraction with the greater numerator is greater.	The fraction with the smaller denominator is greater.	The fraction with the smaller missing piece is greater.

A. To compare the fractions, which strategy works best? Explain.

_____

_____

B. Which fraction is greater? Whose glass has more juice? Explain your answer.

_____

• •

Check Understanding [Math Board]

1 Trent can hold his breath for $\frac{4}{6}$ minute. Is this greater than or less than $\frac{2}{6}$ minute? _____

Draw to show your reasoning.

Compare. Write <, >, or =. Write the strategy you used.

2 $\frac{5}{6}$ ◯ $\frac{2}{3}$ **3** $\frac{3}{8}$ ◯ $\frac{3}{6}$ **4** $\frac{3}{4}$ ◯ $\frac{2}{4}$

_____   _____   _____

On Your Own

5 (MP) **Reason** On a Spelling test, Diane spells $\frac{5}{6}$ of the words correctly. Bill spells $\frac{4}{5}$ of the words correctly. Explain why the missing pieces strategy should work for comparing these the fractions. Which fraction is greater? How do you know?

_____

_____

_____

_____

Compare. Write <, >, or =. Write the strategy you used.

6 $\frac{1}{5}$ ◯ $\frac{1}{8}$

7 $\frac{3}{4}$ ◯ $\frac{5}{4}$

8 $\frac{8}{9}$ ◯ $\frac{3}{4}$

9 **Open Ended** Write and solve a word problem that uses the same numerator strategy to compare two fractions. Include a visual model with your problem.

_____

_____

_____

🔷 I'm in a Learning Mindset!

Which of the following helped me best understand how to compare fractions in this lesson: comparing same denominators, same numerators, drawing a fraction model, or visualizing an image in my head? Explain.

_____

Vocabulary

Choose the correct term from the Vocabulary box to complete the sentence.

1 Use a symbol to complete the comparison.

$\frac{1}{4}$ mile $\bigcirc$ $\frac{1}{2}$ mile

2 The _____ of a fraction tells how many equal parts are in the whole.

3 The _____ of a fraction tells how many equal parts are being counted.

Concepts and Skills

4 (MP) **Use Tools** Megan colors $\frac{5}{6}$ of her sheet of paper. Natasha colors $\frac{2}{6}$ of her paper. The sheets of paper are the same size and shape. Who colors more of her paper? How do you know? Tell what strategy or tool you will use to answer the question, explain your choice, and then find the answer.

_____

_____

_____

5 Doug and Maria each have a waffle. The waffles are the same size and shape. Doug eats $\frac{2}{3}$ of his waffle. Maria eats $\frac{5}{6}$ of her waffle. Who has more waffle left? Explain.

_____

_____

_____

_____

6 Paula and Joey each have equal-sized tortillas. Paula cuts her tortilla into 8 equal pieces and eats 5 of them. Joey cuts her tortilla into 6 equal pieces and eats 5 of them. Who eats less? Explain how you found your answer. Use a drawing to help show your answer.

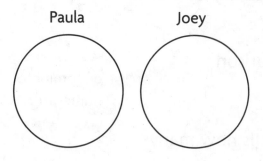

_____

_____

_____

7 What fraction does the number line show?

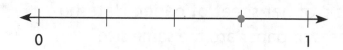

0   1

_____

Label the fraction $\frac{3}{8}$ on the number line.

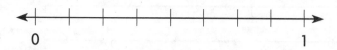

0   1

Write <, >, or = to compare the fractions on the number lines.

 ◯ $\frac{3}{8}$

© Houghton Mifflin Harcourt Publishing Company

Understand Equivalent Fractions

Which square shows a different amount shaded blue?

- Look at each square.

- Write a fraction for about how much of the square is shaded blue.

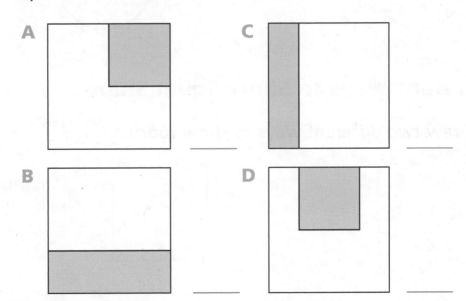

A _____

C _____

B _____

D _____

 Turn and Talk

- Which square does not belong? Explain.

- How does the area of the blue piece in Square A compare to the area of the blue piece in Square C? Explain.

Are You Ready?

Complete these problems to review prior concepts and skills you will need for this module.

Equal Shares

Draw lines to show unequal shares or equal shares.

1 2 unequal shares

2 2 equal shares

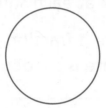

Different Ways to Show Equal Shares

3 Draw two different ways to show fourths.

Fractions of a Whole

Write the fraction that names the shaded part of each shape.

4

5

6

_____   _____   _____

Name _____

Represent Equivalent Fractions with Smaller Parts

(**I Can**) represent a fraction with equal parts that are smaller in size than the equal parts of an equivalent fraction.

Spark Your Learning

Kyra folds a sheet of paper in half and shades 1 of the 2 sections. Julio folds Kyra's sheet in half again. Kyra says $\frac{1}{2}$ of the sheet is shaded. Julio says $\frac{2}{4}$ of the sheet is shaded. Who is correct?

Show and explain your answer.

PAIRS

$\frac{1}{2}$

Kyra: one fold   Julio: two folds

 Turn and Talk After Julio makes his fold, Kyra folds the paper in half one more time. What fraction is now shaded?

Build Understanding

1 Tia folds a square sheet of paper into fourths. She shades $\frac{3}{4}$ of the paper red.

Show how Tia's paper might look in the workspace on the left.

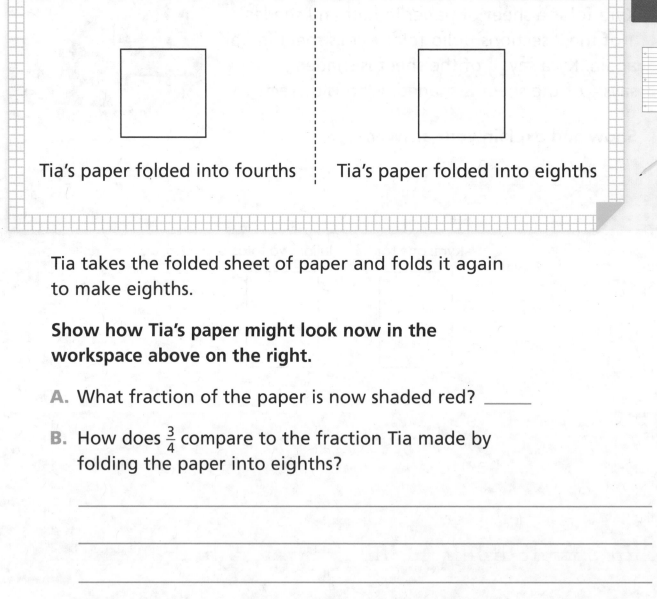

Tia's paper folded into fourths | Tia's paper folded into eighths

Tia takes the folded sheet of paper and folds it again to make eighths.

Show how Tia's paper might look now in the workspace above on the right.

A. What fraction of the paper is now shaded red? _____

B. How does $\frac{3}{4}$ compare to the fraction Tia made by folding the paper into eighths?

_____

_____

_____

Turn and Talk What happens to the size and number of the equal parts each time Tia folds the paper?

2 Alvin folds a strip of paper into thirds and shades $\frac{2}{3}$. Then Alvin folds the same strip again into sixths. Show Alvin's strip folded into thirds and sixths.

thirds ┌─────────────────────┐
       └─────────────────────┘

sixths ┌─────────────────────┐
       └─────────────────────┘

A. Divide the number line to show thirds and sixths. Label the fractions on the number line. Then draw a point to show the part of the strip Alvin shaded.

> **Connect to Vocabulary**
>
> Two or more fractions that name the same amount or distance on a number line are called **equivalent fractions**.

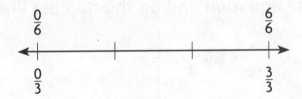

$\frac{0}{6}$ $\frac{6}{6}$

$\frac{0}{3}$ $\frac{3}{3}$

B. What fraction in sixths is equivalent to $\frac{2}{3}$? How do you know that the two fractions are equivalent?

_____

 Turn and Talk Can two fractions with a different number of equal parts be equivalent? Explain.

Check Understanding

1 Shade to show $\frac{1}{4}$. Then draw a line to show an equivalent fraction.

$\frac{1}{4} = \dfrac{\square}{\square}$

2 Draw a point to show $\frac{1}{2}$. Then write the equivalent fraction.

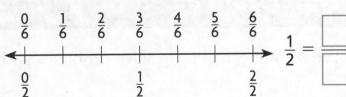

$\frac{0}{6}$ $\frac{1}{6}$ $\frac{2}{6}$ $\frac{3}{6}$ $\frac{4}{6}$ $\frac{5}{6}$ $\frac{6}{6}$

$\frac{0}{2}$ $\frac{1}{2}$ $\frac{2}{2}$

$\frac{1}{2} = \dfrac{\square}{\square}$

On Your Own

3 (MP) **Use Tools** Brian shades $\frac{1}{3}$ of a circle green. Show an equivalent fraction on the same-sized circle.

Brian's Circle   **Your Circle**

- Write the equivalent fraction. $\frac{1}{3} = \dfrac{\boxed{}}{\boxed{}}$

- Explain why the fractions shown by Brian's circle and your circle are equivalent.

Locate and draw a point on the number line for the fraction. Then write the equivalent fraction in the equation and on the number line.

4 $\frac{2}{4} = \dfrac{\boxed{}}{\boxed{}}$

5 $\frac{2}{3} = \dfrac{\boxed{}}{\boxed{}}$

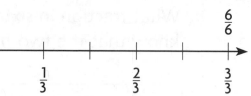

6 (MP) **Reason** Explain why $\frac{3}{3} = \frac{4}{4}$ for the same-sized whole. Draw to justify your answer.

I'm in a Learning Mindset!

What tools can I use to solve problems with equivalent fractions?

Represent Equivalent Fractions with Larger Parts

(**I Can**) represent a fraction with equal parts that are larger in size than the equal parts of an equivalent fraction.

Spark Your Learning

Thea is a landscaper. According to her design, $\frac{2}{3}$ of the garden should contain red roses. She plants red roses in $\frac{4}{6}$ of her new garden, not $\frac{2}{3}$. Does Thea make a mistake?

Show a way to solve the problem.

PAIRS

 Turn and Talk Thea's design and garden represent the same-sized whole. How do the number of parts and the size of the parts compare in each fraction?

Build Understanding

1 At soccer practice, Coach Penny draws a diagram in which she divides the field into 8 equal-sized zones. The 6 zones closest to the goal are the scoring zones.

Use Coach Penny's diagram to show the area she uses for the scoring zones.

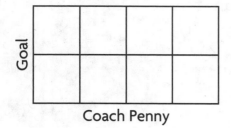
Coach Penny

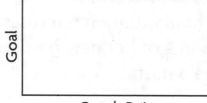
Coach Ruiz

Coach Ruiz divides the same field into 4 equal-sized zones. Coach Ruiz's scoring zones are the 3 zones closest to the goal. Use Coach Ruiz's diagram to show the area he uses for the scoring zones.

A. What fraction can you write for the area of the field that Coach Penny uses for the scoring zones? _____

B. What fraction can you write to represent Coach Ruiz's scoring zones? _____

C. How do the fractions compare for the area of Coach Penny's and Coach Ruiz's scoring zones? Explain.

_____

_____

 Turn and Talk Which coach's soccer field diagram has a greater number of scoring zones? In which diagram are the scoring zones greater in size? Explain.

2 Two relay teams race across Lomas Park. The Red Team divides the distance equally among 6 runners. The Blue Team divides the distance equally among 3 runners.

A. Show how both teams divide the race into equal distances.

Red Team [ ]   Blue Team [ ]

B. The first 4 runners for the Red Team and the first 2 runners for the Blue Team complete their parts of the race. Use the drawings to show the distances that the teams complete.

C. Locate and draw a point to show how much of the race each team completes. Complete the number line and show the fractions.

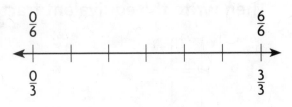

D. How do the fractions of the race that each team completes compare? Which team completes more of the race? Explain.

_____

 Turn and Talk When the same whole is divided into a fewer total number of equal parts, are the parts larger or smaller? Explain.

Check Understanding 📋 Math Board

1 Divide and shade the model to show an equivalent fraction.

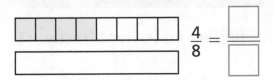

$$\frac{4}{8} = \frac{\square}{\square}$$

2 Draw a point to show $\frac{2}{6}$. Then write the equivalent fraction.

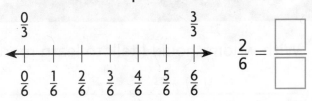

$$\frac{2}{6} = \frac{\square}{\square}$$

On Your Own

3 (MP) **Attend to Precision** Mrs. Ash shades $\frac{1}{2}$ of a rectangle. Will shades 3 of 6 sections of a same-sized rectangle.

Will says that the 3 of 6 sections he shades are equivalent to $\frac{1}{2}$, so both rectangles have the same area shaded. Is he correct? Explain why or why not.

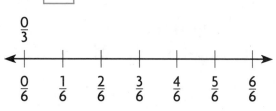

Mrs. Ash   Will

_____

_____

Locate and draw a point on the number line for the fraction. Then write the equivalent fraction.

4 $\frac{6}{6} = \dfrac{\boxed{}}{\boxed{}}$

$\frac{0}{3}$

$\frac{0}{6}$ $\frac{1}{6}$ $\frac{2}{6}$ $\frac{3}{6}$ $\frac{4}{6}$ $\frac{5}{6}$ $\frac{6}{6}$

5 $\frac{4}{8} = \dfrac{\boxed{}}{\boxed{}}$

$\frac{0}{2}$ $\frac{2}{2}$

$\frac{0}{8}$ $\frac{1}{8}$ $\frac{2}{8}$ $\frac{3}{8}$ $\frac{4}{8}$ $\frac{5}{8}$ $\frac{6}{8}$ $\frac{7}{8}$ $\frac{8}{8}$

6 (MP) **Use Structure** Tim says that $\frac{2}{8}$ of his water bottle is filled. John says that $\frac{1}{4}$ of the bottle is filled. Are the two fractions equivalent? Draw a visual model to support your answer.

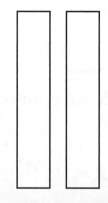

_____

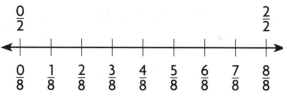

I'm in a Learning Mindset!

With whom should I talk to learn more about finding equivalent fractions?

_____

Name _____

Recognize and Generate Equivalent Fractions

(I Can) represent a fraction with equal parts that are smaller or larger in size than the equal parts of an equivalent fraction.

Spark Your Learning

Meghan wants to save some of the lasagna she makes for her cousin Jeremy. She divides the pan of lasagna into fourths and saves $\frac{2}{4}$ of the pan for Jeremy.

Can you think of two other ways Meghan can divide the lasagna into equal-sized smaller or larger parts and still save the same amount for Jeremy?

Show how to divide the lasagna for each pan. Shade the parts that Meghan saves for Jeremy. Explain how you know that Jeremy will get the same amount of lasagna for each pan.

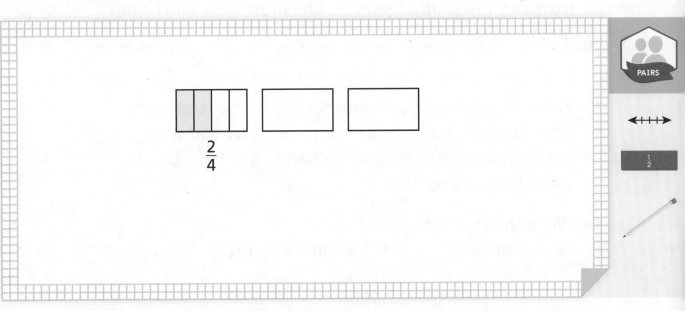

$\frac{2}{4}$

PAIRS

$\frac{1}{2}$

Turn and Talk How can you check to see if two fractions are equivalent?

Build Understanding

1 Rico's band eats pizza after band practice each week. On Friday, the band eats $\frac{6}{8}$ of a cheese pizza. The next week, the band eats the same amount of a same-sized vegetable pizza cut into 4 equal pieces. What fraction of the vegetable pizza does the band eat?

Show one way to solve the problem.

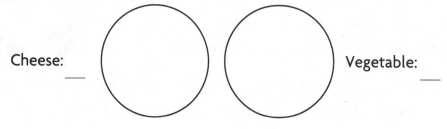

Cheese: ___   Vegetable: ___

A. How can you draw lines to divide the two pizzas? Into how many pieces will you divide each pizza?

_____

_____

B. How can you shade the pizzas to show how much the band eats? _____

_____

C. What fraction can you write for the amount of each pizza that the band eats? Label each pizza to show the fraction of each pizza the band eats. How do these fractions compare? _____

D. Write the fractions. Write >, <, or =.
The band eats ____ of the vegetable pizza.

 Turn and Talk Two fractions are equivalent. The first fraction has a greater denominator. What does that tell you about the numerator of the first fraction?

© Houghton Mifflin Harcourt Publishing Company • Image Credit: ©Evikka/Shutterstock

Step It Out

2 Lea runs $\frac{3}{2}$ mile. Roxie runs the same distance on a track laid out in fourths of a mile. How far does Roxie run?

A. Complete the number line.

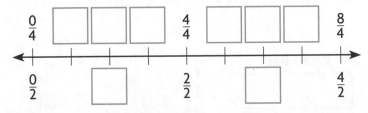

B. Locate and draw a point on the number line to show how far Lea and Roxie run. Write the equivalent fraction.

$\frac{3}{2}$ mile = _____

3 Draw circles to show equal groups. Find equivalent fractions for the shaded area of the shapes. Write the fractions.

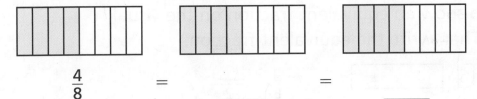

$\frac{4}{8}$ = _____ = _____

....

Check Understanding

Math Board

1 Circle equal groups to find an equivalent fraction for the shaded area.

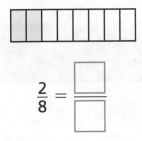

$\frac{2}{8} = \dfrac{\boxed{}}{\boxed{}}$

2 Draw a point on the number line to find an equivalent fraction.

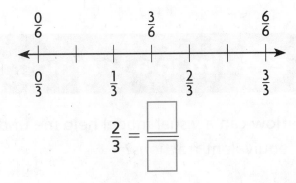

$\frac{2}{3} = \dfrac{\boxed{}}{\boxed{}}$

On Your Own

3 (MP) **Use Structure** Robert eats $\frac{1}{3}$ of a granola bar. Ken eats the same amount of his granola bar. Both granola bars are the same size. Ken divides his bar into sixths. What fraction of a granola bar does Ken eat? Show how much Ken and Robert eat. Write an equivalent fraction.

Robert's Bar   **Ken's Bar**

$\frac{1}{3} = \dfrac{\boxed{}}{\boxed{}}$

4 Locate and draw a point on the number line. Then write the equivalent fraction.

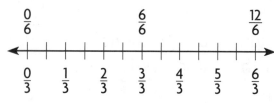

$\frac{4}{3} = \dfrac{\boxed{}}{\boxed{}}$

5 Shade to show an equivalent fraction on the visual model. Then write the equivalent fraction.

$\frac{3}{6} = \dfrac{\boxed{}}{2}$

6 **STEM** A wheel and an axle turn together in the direction shown. One wheel has 4 spokes and makes $\frac{3}{4}$ of a turn. The other wheel has 8 spokes. Shade to show how far the 8-spoke wheel turns. Write the equivalent fraction.

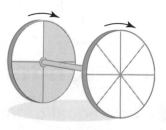

$\frac{3}{4} = \dfrac{\boxed{}}{\boxed{}}$

I'm in a Learning Mindset!

How can a visual model help me understand how to generate equivalent fractions?

Vocabulary

Choose the correct term from the Vocabulary box to complete the sentence.

Vocabulary

equivalent
  fractions
equal parts
numerator
denominator

1 The _____ shows the number of parts into which the whole is divided.

2 Two or more fractions that name the same

amount are _____ .

Concepts and Skills

3 What fraction does the point on the first number

line represent? _____

Draw a point on the second number line that is equivalent to the point on the first number line.

Write <, >, or = to compare the fractions on the two number lines.

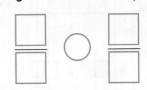

4 (MP) **Use Tools** Match the equivalent fractions. Tell what strategy or tool you will use to solve the problem, explain your choice, and then find the

answers. _____

$\frac{1}{2}$ •   • $\frac{1}{3}$

$\frac{4}{3}$ •   • $\frac{2}{4}$

$\frac{2}{6}$ •   • $\frac{8}{6}$

5 Reese draws lines to divide a circle and shades one part. Divide the same-sized circle another way to show an equivalent fraction.

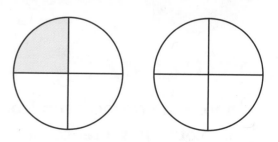

Write the two fractions.
Write <, >, or =.

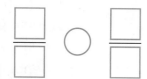

6 Match the equivalent fractions.

Fraction	$\frac{1}{3}$	$\frac{1}{2}$	$\frac{2}{3}$	$\frac{6}{8}$
$\frac{4}{6}$	☐	☐	☐	☐
$\frac{3}{4}$	☐	☐	☐	☐
$\frac{2}{6}$	☐	☐	☐	☐
$\frac{2}{4}$	☐	☐	☐	☐

7 Write two equivalent fractions represented by point *A*.

_____

Write two equivalent fractions represented by point *B*.

_____

Measurement and Data

Playground Designer

© Houghton Mifflin Harcourt Publishing Company • Image Credit: ©Masuti/Getty Images

Playground designers have a great job, but a lot of work goes into designing a playground. The designers have to make each playground safe as well as fun.

Some playgrounds are unique. For example, there is a playground in Utah that has a 30-foot tall pyramid.

Did you know that playgrounds provide more than just fun for kids? They are a place for "full body" workouts that include exercises that strengthen arms, legs, shoulders, and more. All that exercise also stimulates brain activity.

STEM Task:

Playground designers need to make equipment strong enough for several children to use. Your task is to decide which shape to use to support a play house.

Work with a partner to make three structures from sturdy paper. Fold or roll the paper to form a cube, a rectangular box, and a tube. Tape your structures together, then stand them up. Place books on the shapes to see which ones can support the most weight.

Learning Mindset

Resilience Responds to Feedback

Learning to give feedback and listen to feedback is an important skill. Listening to feedback can help you figure out what you still need to learn or where you are making mistakes. When you give feedback, you should focus on helping your partner get better at something. Encouraging others is a form of feedback that is helpful when they are discouraged or frustrated.

Reflect

Q What feedback did you get from your partner as you were doing the activity? How did you use the feedback?

Q What feedback did you provide to your partner? Remember, not all feedback has to be a suggestion. Encouragement is another type of feedback.

17 Liquid Volume and Mass

What object weighs the most?

Basketball   **Soccer Ball**   **Bowling Ball**   **Volleyball**   **Beach Ball**

Use the clues to order the balls from lightest (1) to heaviest (5).

- Write the name of each ball on a sticky note. Then arrange them as you read each clue.

Clues:

- The basketball is heavier than the soccer ball.

- The volleyball is lighter than the soccer ball.

- The bowling ball is heavier than the basketball.

- The beach ball is lighter than the volleyball.

 Turn and Talk

- Miguel says that the basketball and beach ball should weigh the same because they are about the same size. Does his statement make sense? Explain.

Are You Ready?

Complete these problems to review prior concepts and skills you will need for this module.

Measure to the Nearest Inch

 Use the ruler to measure the length to the nearest inch.

The marker is about _____ inches long.

Estimate with Benchmarks

The square has sides that are 1 inch in length. Use the square to estimate the length of each object.

about _____ inches

about _____ inches

Compare Numbers

Compare the numbers. Write <, >, or =.

 57 ◯ 54   93 ◯ 80   74 ◯ 75

Name

Estimate and Measure Liquid Volume

(I Can) use metric units to estimate and measure liquid volume.

Spark Your Learning

Describe a situation in which each container might have been filled. In each description, be sure to compare the amount of liquid in the container to the size of the container. The same amount of liquid is in each container.

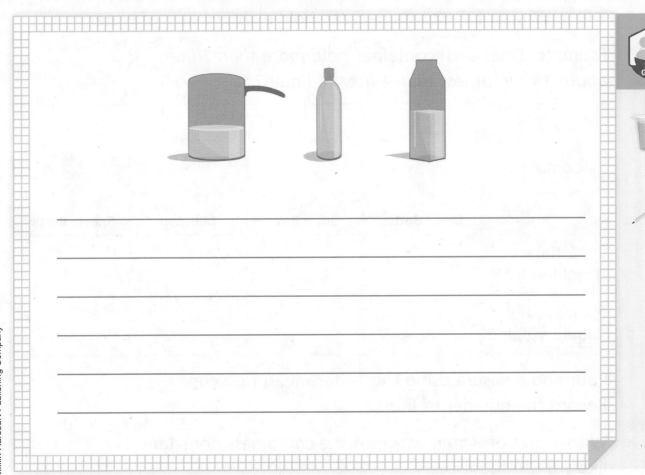

SMALL GROUPS

Turn and Talk Which container can hold the greatest amount of liquid? Which container holds the least amount of liquid? Explain.

Build Understanding

This metric measuring cup is filled with 1 liter of water.

A mug holds *less than* **1 liter.**

A bottle of juice holds *about* **1 liter.**

A paint can holds *more than* **1 liter.**

1 Tam pours 1 liter of water into a container that holds exactly 1 liter. Which of the containers can hold exactly 1 liter of water?

Estimate. Does each container hold *more than 1 liter,* *about 1 liter,* or *less than 1 liter* of liquid?

Container	Drink Bottle	Juice Box	Milk Jug	Sports Bottle
Estimate Liquid Volume				
Measure Liquid Volume				

Pour and measure using the 1-liter measuring cup. Record the number of liters.

With 1 liter of water, which of the containers does Tam likely fill to the top?

 Turn and Talk What is the order of the containers from least to greatest liquid volume?

Step It Out

Reza   **Joy**

2 ▶ Reza and Joy have same-sized containers filled with different amounts of water, as shown. Reza's container is marked in liters (L). About how much water, in liters (L), does Joy's container have?

A. Find a unit name on Reza's container. This is the unit of liquid volume that is being used.	The unit shown is L. L stands for liter.
B. Find the measurement marks on Reza's container. How much does each line stand for? What numbers label the lines?	Each measurement mark is labeled with a number 1, 2, 3, 4, 5. So, each mark stands for 1 liter. This is the scale.
C. Find the amount of water in Reza's container.	The water in Reza's container is at the mark for 3. Reza's container has about _____ of water.
D. How do the two containers compare in size?	The containers are the same size.
E. Estimate the amount of water in Joy's container by using the marks on Reza's container.	The water in Joy's container matches a level of about _____ in Reza's container.
F. About how much water is in Joy's container?	Joy's container has about _____ of water.

• •

Check Understanding

1 How many liters of water are in the container

shown? Estimate to the nearest liter. _____

On Your Own

2 (MP) **Use Tools** Mindi and Kan have same-sized containers filled with different amounts of water, as shown. Mindi's container has 20 liters of water. About how much water, in liters, does Kan's container have?

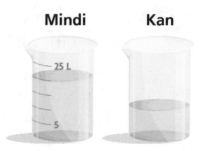
Mindi   Kan

_____

Estimate the liquid volume of the liquid in the container. Write _more than 1 liter_, _about 1 liter_, or _less than 1 liter_.

3 vase

4 soup bowl

5 pail

_____   _____   _____

6 (MP) **Reason** About how many liters of water are in the container?

100 L
60
20

_____

🔢 I'm in a Learning Mindset!

How do I feel about my learning when I estimate and measure liquid volume?

_____

Name

Estimate and Measure Mass

(I Can) use metric units to estimate and measure the mass of objects.

Spark Your Learning

Ronan packs his backpack for school. Today, he has a book, a folder, a paper clip, and an apple to pack. Compare the objects using a pan balance. Make a drawing for each comparison. How can you describe the ways in which the objects compare to one another?

Turn and Talk On a pan balance, how would the paper clip compare to the apple? Explain how you got your answer.

Build Understanding

1 Look around the classroom for the items listed in the chart.

Estimate the mass of each object. Then use a pan balance, gram masses, and kilogram masses to measure the mass of each object.

Item	Estimate Mass	Measure Mass
3-hole punch		
eraser		
paper clip		
stapler		
pen		
pencil		
ruler		

A. Describe how your estimates compare to your measurements. Explain.

_____

_____

_____

B. Write the order of the objects from the least mass to the greatest mass.

_____

 Turn and Talk How do you know when to use grams and when to use kilograms when you measure the mass of an object?

Name _____

Step It Out

2 A baker orders a basket of apples and a wooden spoon to make apple pies. Which unit would be better for measuring the mass of each object?

	Benchmarks
A. Think about objects you know—a textbook and a paper clip. Use these objects as benchmarks for mass.	about 1 gram about 1 kilogram
B. Estimate which benchmark's mass is closer to the mass of the basket of apples. Then write *grams* or *kilograms*.	Measure the mass of the basket of apples using _____.
C. Estimate which benchmark's mass is closer to the mass of the wooden spoon. Then write *grams* or *kilograms*.	Measure the mass of the wooden spoon using _____.

Check Understanding 🔲 Math Board

1 List these objects in order from the least mass to the greatest mass: orange, sneaker, marker.

_____

**Choose the unit you would use to measure the mass.
Write *grams* or *kilograms*.**

2 box of crayons   **3** packed backpack   **4** banana

            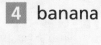

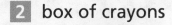   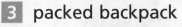   

On Your Own

5 (MP) **Use Tools** Tomas is comparing the masses of four different toys. He already knows that the bag of marbles has the greatest mass. He wants to order his toys from greatest mass to least mass.

- Write *greater than* or *less than*.

  The mass of the cube puzzle is _____ the mass of the yo-yo.

  The mass of the cube puzzle is _____ the mass of the football.

- List the toys in order from greatest mass to least mass.

  _____

Choose the unit you would use to measure the mass. Write *grams* or *kilograms*.

6 melon

_____

7 cell phone

_____

8 keychain

_____

⊕ I'm in a Learning Mindset!

Do I understand how to estimate and measure mass? What do I still need to work on?

_____

Name

Solve Problems About Liquid Volume and Mass

(I Can) solve word problems that involve liquid volume and mass.

Step It Out

1 Ava fills the 100-L container to the mark shown to water a garden. She will use water from the 100-L container to fill the empty pan on the right to the top mark.

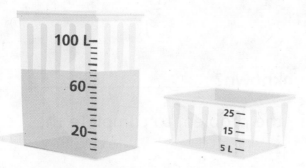

A. Complete the bar model to show the amount of water in each container after Ava fills the pan.

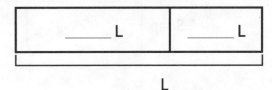

B. What equation can you write to represent how much water will be in the 100-L container? _____

C. How many liters of water will be left in the 100-L container? _____

 Turn and Talk How did you decide what equation to write to solve the problem?

Step It Out

2 Pete ships a care package to his brother at camp. The mass of the soap bar is 58 fewer grams than the mass of a tube of toothpaste. What is the mass of the tube of toothpaste?

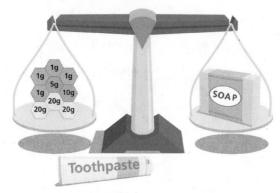

A. What information is unknown? _____

B. Use the information in the problem to complete the bar model.

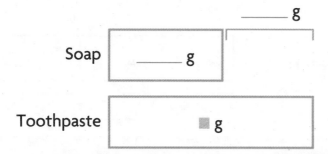

C. Use the bar model to write an equation to solve the problem.

_____

D. What is the mass of the tube of toothpaste?

_____

Turn and Talk How did you decide what equation to use to solve the problem?

3 Pete ships some markers to his brother at camp. Each marker has the mass shown. What is the mass of 6 markers?

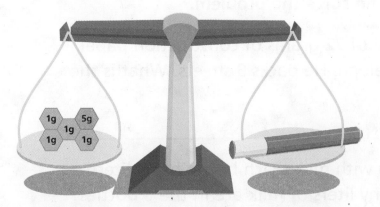

A. Make a drawing to represent the problem.

B. Complete the bar model to represent the problem.

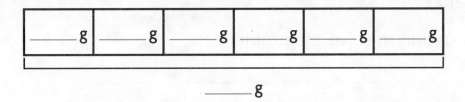

C. Write a multiplication equation to represent the problem. _____

D. What is the mass of 6 markers? _____

 Turn and Talk Describe the visual model and the equation you used to solve the problem.

Check Understanding

Write an equation and solve the problem.

1 Han packs a total of 72 grams of construction paper sheets in an envelope. He packs 9 sheets. What is the mass of each sheet?

_____

2 Jen fills 6 bottles with milk. Each bottle has 3 liters of milk. How many liters of milk are in the 6 bottles?

_____

On Your Own

3 (MP) **Model with Mathematics** Jamal's car has a full tank of gas. Then he uses 24 liters of gas. There are 16 liters of gas left in the tank. How many liters of gas are in a full tank?

- Write an equation to solve the problem.

_____

- How many liters of gas are in a full tank?

_____

4 **STEM** An ice cube has a mass of 28 grams. After it is left out on a warm counter, it has a mass of 13 grams. How many fewer grams of mass does the ice cube have after being left on the counter? Write an equation to solve the problem.

_____

5 (MP) **Model with Mathematics**
Each ball of yarn has the mass shown.
Esther buys several balls of yarn that
have a mass of 56 grams. How many
balls of yarn does she buy?

- Complete the bar model to show
  the problem.

_____ balls of yarn

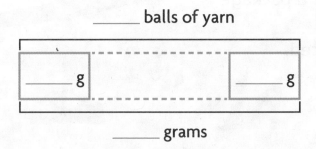

_____ g   _____ g

_____ grams

- Write an equation to show the problem.

_____

Esther buys _____ balls of yarn.

6 (MP) **Reason** A shower uses 7 liters of water in 1 minute.
How many liters of water would a 7-minute shower
use? Explain how you found your answer.

_____

_____

7 **Open Ended** Write and solve a
word problem about the mass
of some paint brushes.

_____

_____

_____

_____

On Your Own

8 (MP) **Reason** Naomi is shipping packages to customers. Each package has a mass of 4 kilograms. There are 7 packages. What is the mass of the 7 packages?

_____

9 (MP) **Use Tools** If Teri places a package of crackers on the left pan, the two pans will be balanced. What is the mass of the package of crackers?

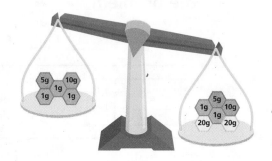

_____

10 (MP) **Use Structure** A kiwi fruit has a mass that is 67 grams more than the mass of a strawberry. The mass of the kiwi fruit is 83 grams. What is the mass of the strawberry?

_____

11 (MP) **Model with Mathematics** A soccer team has an 18-liter water cooler. Each player has a 2-liter water bottle. Write and solve a problem about the water cooler and the water bottles.

_____

_____

_____

_____

Module 17

Review

Vocabulary

Choose the correct term from the Vocabulary box.

1 A bottle of juice holds about 1 _____ of liquid.

2 _____ is the amount of liquid in a container.

3 A paper clip has a mass of about 1 _____.

Concepts and Skills

4 About how many liters of water are in the container shown? Estimate to the nearest liter. _____

5 (MP) **Use Tools** Stella's baseball cap has a mass that is less than the mass of a brick but greater than the mass of a ring. Which mass could be the mass of her baseball cap? Tell the strategy or tool you will use to answer the question, explain your choice, and then find the answer.

Ⓐ 5 grams   Ⓒ 1 kilogram

Ⓑ 100 grams   Ⓓ 2 kilograms

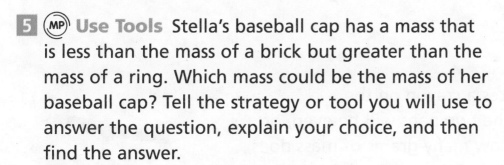

6 Fiona has some beads that are all the same. Each bead has the mass shown. The total mass of the beads is 56 grams. How many beads does Fiona have?

Ⓐ 7   Ⓑ 8   Ⓒ 48   Ⓓ 64

7 Select all the items that have a mass that would best be measured using grams.

Ⓐ

Ⓓ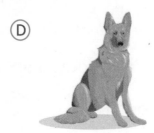

Ⓑ

Ⓔ

Ⓒ

8 If Ming places a crayon on the right pan, the two pans will be even, or balanced. How many grams of mass does the crayon have?

_____

9 Brian and Yuri have same-sized containers with different amounts of water. About how many fewer liters of water does Yuri's container have?

Brian   Yuri

Ⓐ 50 liters   Ⓒ 150 liters

Ⓑ 100 liters   Ⓓ 200 liters

Represent and Interpret Data

What is **missing** from the graph?

- Sam and Max ask students in their class to choose their favorite color. The choices are red, blue, yellow, and green. They share the results in a table.

- Next, Max and Sam start to make a bar graph. Help them complete the graph.

Color	Number of Students
Red	6
Blue	4
Yellow	3
Green	2

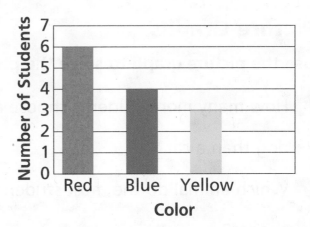

 Turn and Talk

- The bar graph is also missing a title. What would be a good title for this graph?

- If you and a partner choose your favorite color, how would that change the graph?

Are You Ready?

Complete these problems to review prior concepts and skills you will need for this module.

Read a Tally Chart

Complete the tally chart. Then use the tally chart to answer the questions.

1 How many more miles did Lucas bike on Thursday than on Tuesday?

_____

2 How many miles did Lucas bike

in all? _____

Miles Lucas Biked		
Day	Tally	Total
Monday	卌 I	
Tuesday	III	
Wednesday	卌 II	
Thursday	卌	

Picture Graphs

Use the picture graph to solve the problems.

3 How many more students choose a

dog than a cat? _____

4 Which animal do the most students

choose? _____

Favorite Animals				
Cat	Cat			
Dog	Dog	Dog	Dog	Dog
Bird	Bird	Bird		
Bunny	Bunny	Bunny	Bunny	

Bar Graphs

Use the bar graph to solve the problems.

5 Which subject did the fewest students

choose? _____

6 How many fewer students chose art

than reading? _____

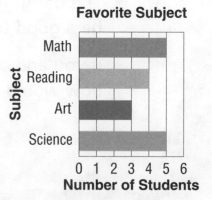

Favorite Subject

Subject: Math, Reading, Art, Science

0 1 2 3 4 5 6
Number of Students

Name _____

Use Picture Graphs

(I Can) use data in a picture graph to solve *how many more* and *how many less* problems.

Spark Your Learning

Ms. Marin's students are showing data that they collected. On what topic might the students have collected information?

Use your topic idea to complete the graph.

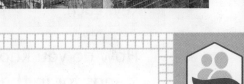

PAIRS

	🐾 🐾
	🐾 🐾 🐾 🐾
	🐾 🐾 🐾

 Turn and Talk Discuss your scenario with a partner. Ask your partner questions that can be answered by using the graph.

© Houghton Mifflin Harcourt Publishing Company • Image Credit: ©Getty Images

Build Understanding

Connect to Vocabulary

A **picture graph** uses symbols to show and compare information. Picture graphs have a **key** that tells the number of objects each symbol represents.

1 Ami records the number of each type of tree she sees.

Trees in the Park	
Pine	🌲 🌲
Maple	🌲
Willow	🌲 🌲 🌲
Palm	🌲 🌲 🌲 ⌐
Oak	🌲 🌲
Key: Each 🌲 = 2 trees.	

A. How do you know how many trees each tree symbol stands for in the graph?

_____

B. What equation can you write to find the number of willow trees Ami sees? How many willow trees does Ami see?

_____

C. If 🌲 stands for 2 trees, what does ⌐ stand for in the graph? Explain.

_____

D. How can you find the number of palm trees Ami sees?

_____

_____

 Turn and Talk How would the data be displayed for Pine, Maple, and Oak if the tree symbol represented 4 trees?

2 Rowan records the types of plants sold at the store on Saturday.

Plants Sold	
Cactus	🌱🌱
Aloe	🌱🌱🌱🌱
Violet	🌱🌱🌱🌱
Bamboo	🌱🌱🌱
Lily	🌱🌱🌱
Key: Each 🌱 = 4 plants.	

A. What equation can you write to find the number of aloe plants sold? How many aloe plants were sold?

_____

_____ aloe plants

B. What equations can you write to find the number of bamboo plants sold?
How many bamboo plants were sold?

_____

_____ bamboo plants

C. How can you find how many more aloe plants than bamboo plants were sold?

_____

_____

 Turn and Talk How did you know which operation to use to compare the amounts?

• •

Check Understanding

Use the picture graph above.

1 How many fewer cactus plants than lily plants were sold?

_____

2 How many more aloe plants than violet plants were sold?

_____

On Your Own

(MP) **Reason** Use the graph for 3–7.

Dean surveys his friends about the number of books they read in the summer.

3 How many books did the 5 friends read?

_____

4 How many more books did Lamar read than Katie?

_____

5 How many friends read fewer than 10 books?

_____

6 How many fewer books did Andy read than Cole?

_____

Class Reading Log			
Cole	☐	☐	☐
Patti	☐	☐	
Katie	☐	☐	
Andy	☐		
Lamar	☐	☐	☐
Key: Each ☐ = 5 books.			

7 **Open Ended** Write a question that can be answered using information from the graph.

_____

_____

🔶 I'm in a Learning Mindset!

How does using multiplication to find the total number in each picture graph category make me feel about my learning?

_____

_____

Name _____

Make Picture Graphs

(I Can) draw a scaled picture graph to solve *how many more* and *how many less* problems.

Spark Your Learning

Victor makes the table at the right. He uses it to record the types of projects that the third grade classes would like to do for community service.

Which type of community service would you do?

Project	Votes
Pull Weeds	15
Rake Leaves	18
Wash Cars	12
Clean Up	21

Make a representation of the data.

PAIRS

 Turn and Talk How are your representations alike and how are they different?

Build Understanding

1 Mr. Hom counts and records in a table the number of tools he has.

Tool Supply	
Tools	Number
Screwdrivers	8
Wrenches	12
Bolts	24
Nuts	18

A. How can you tell what a picture graph is about?

_____

_____

B. How many should one symbol represent? Choose a number greater than 1.

_____

Think: Half of the symbol stands for half the value of the whole symbol.

C. How many symbols will you draw for each tool?

_____

_____

Make a picture graph of the data.

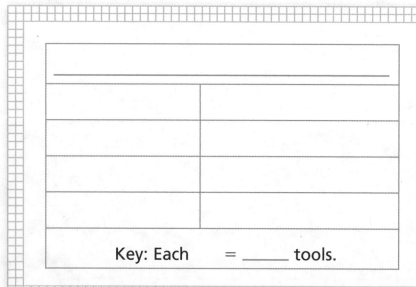

Key: Each ____ = _____ tools.	

 Turn and Talk What equation can you write to find how many more bolts than nuts Mr. Hom has?

Step It Out

2 Use the table to record data for the number of each item in your classroom.

3 Use the data in the table to make a picture graph.

Classroom Items	
Item	**Number**
Bins	
Closets	
Desks	
Posters	
Shelves	

A. Write the title. Write the items in the left column. Choose a symbol.

B. Choose a number greater than 1 for what the symbol represents.

Think: Do you need to use half of a symbol?

C. Draw the symbols in each row.

Key: Each ____ = _____ items.

D. What equation can you write to find how many fewer closets than desks there are? Solve.

_____.

Check Understanding

Use the picture graph above.

1 How would the number of symbols change if the number for your key was half?

On Your Own

(MP) **Attend to Precision** Use the information for 2–5.

The students in Ms. Dover's class try to solve a math challenge every week. Ms. Dover records the number of students who solve the challenge.

Weekly Math Challenge	
Weeks	Students
Week 1	15
Week 2	25
Week 3	10
Week 4	5

2 Make a picture graph that shows the data. How will you decide which number to use for your key?

_____

_____

Week 1	
Week 2	
Week 3	
Week 4	

Key: Each ___ = _____ students.

3 How many more students solved the math challenge in Week 1 than in Week 3?

_____

4 How many fewer students solved the math challenge in Week 4 than in Week 2? _____

5 (MP) **Reason** Alma will use a symbol of a smiley face to stand for 5 students. How should a row look for Week 2? Explain.

_____

_____

 I'm in a Learning Mindset!

What do I understand about making a picture graph?

_____

_____

Name _____

Use Bar Graphs

(**I Can**) use data in a scaled bar graph to solve *how many more* and *how many less* problems.

Spark Your Learning

Mr. Mason's students are showing data that they collected. On what topic might the students have collected information?

_____

_____

_____

Use your idea to complete the graph.

Which is your

favorite _____?

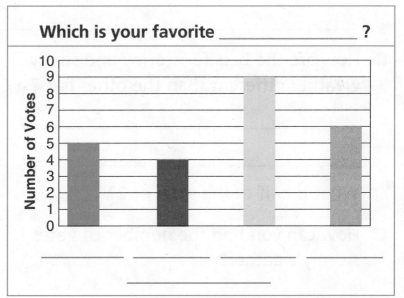

Which is your favorite _____ ?

Turn and Talk Discuss your scenario with a partner. Ask your partner questions that can be answered by using the graph.

Build Understanding

1 Vin asks students which kind of weather is their favorite and makes a bar graph.

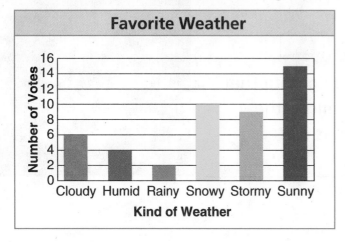

A. How do you know the scale of the bar graph? Explain.

_____

_____

B. How are the bars for stormy and sunny weather different than the other bars?

_____

_____

What is half of the scale of 2? _____

C. How can you find the number of votes for stormy weather?

_____

_____

 Turn and Talk What equation can you write to find how many more votes are for stormy weather than cloudy weather? Explain.

Step It Out

2 Kel surveys students about which kind of movie is their favorite and makes a bar graph.

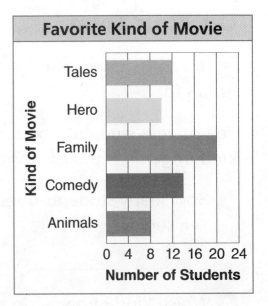

Favorite Kind of Movie

A. What do you notice about the scale?

_____

B. Write an equation to find the number of students who choose family movies.

_____

C. If each space stands for 4 students, what does halfway between the space stand for in the graph? Explain.

_____

Connect to Vocabulary

A **horizontal bar graph** uses bars that go in the direction from left to right.

D. Write equations to find the number of students who choose comedy movies.

_____

E. How can you find how many fewer students choose comedy movies than family movies?

_____

Check Understanding

Use the bar graph above.

1 How many more students choose comedy than hero movies?

_____

2 How many fewer students choose tales than family movies?

_____

On Your Own

 Use Structure **Use the bar graph for 3–7.**

Yee surveys students about which kind of game is their favorite.

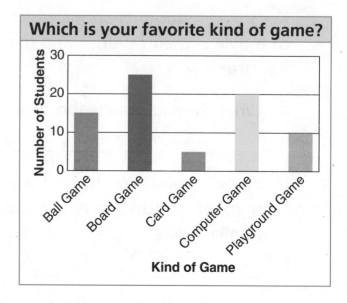

Which is your favorite kind of game?

3 How many students does Yee survey?

_____

4 Which kind of game do the greatest number of students

choose? _____

5 How many more students choose computer game

than ball game? _____

6 How many fewer students choose card game than

computer game? _____

7 **Model with Mathematics** If the scale showed counting by 2s, how would the bars change?

_____

_____

I'm in a Learning Mindset!

How am I adjusting to the idea of displaying data in bar graphs instead of picture graphs?

_____

Name

Make Bar Graphs

(I Can) draw a scaled bar graph to solve *how many more* and *how many less* problems.

Spark Your Learning

Mrs. Vern's students collect the survey results shown in the tally chart.

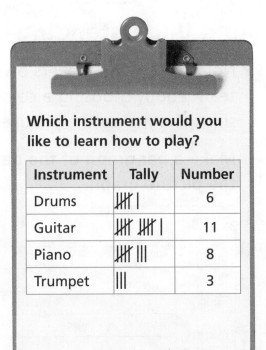

Which instrument would you like to learn how to play?

Instrument	Tally	Number
Drums	IIII I	6
Guitar	IIII IIII I	11
Piano	IIII III	8
Trumpet	III	3

Make a representation of the data.

SMALL GROUPS

Turn and Talk How are your representations alike and different?

Build Understanding

1 Nola surveys the players on her soccer team about choosing a color for the team shirt. She makes the picture graph shown.

Make a bar graph of the data shown in the picture graph.

Votes for Team Shirt Color	
Color	**Number of Votes**
Blue	●●●●◖
Green	●●
Purple	●●●
Red	●◖

Key: Each ● = 2 votes.

A. What number do you count by on the scale?

_____

B. How do you know the height to draw each bar?

_____

_____

_____

C. What equation can you write to find how many more votes blue receives than red?

_____

 Turn and Talk Compare your bar graph display with the picture graph display. How are the displays alike and how are they different?

Step It Out

2 Choose a survey question. Include 3 or 4 answer choices for your question. Decide how you will record the answers. Take a survey of your classmates.

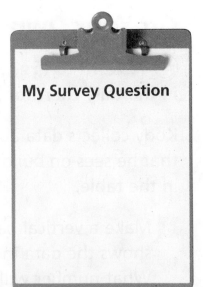

My Survey Question

3 You can make a horizontal bar graph to show the data that you collected.

A. Choose a title. Label the categories.

B. Choose a scale that is greater than 1.

What number will you count by? _____

C. Label your scale.

D. Draw each bar.

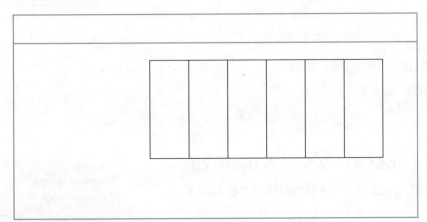

Check Understanding [Math Board]

Use the bar graph you made to answer the questions.

1 If one classmate's answer changes, how would your bars change?

_____

_____

2 Write a *how many fewer* problem. Then solve your problem.

_____

_____

On Your Own

Shapes Seen on Buildings

Shape	Tally
Circle	卌 卌 卌
Rectangle	卌 卌 卌 卌
Triangle	卌

(MP) **Attend to Precision** Use the data in the tally chart for 3–6.

Kody collects data about the kind of shapes that he sees on buildings. His data is shown in the table.

3 Make a vertical bar graph that shows the data in the table. What number will you count by for the scale?

_____

4 How many more rectangles does Kody see than triangles?

_____

5 How many fewer triangles than circles does Kody see?

_____

6 (MP) **Reason** Suppose Kody sees 5 more circles and 5 more triangles. How would the bars change? Explain.

_____

_____

 I'm in a Learning Mindset!

How can I effectively give and receive feedback about making graphs?

_____

_____

Name _____

Use Line Plots to Display Measurement Data

(I Can) use a line plot to display measurement data.

Spark Your Learning

Nina measures the length of 2 candles, each from a different package. What is the length of each candle?

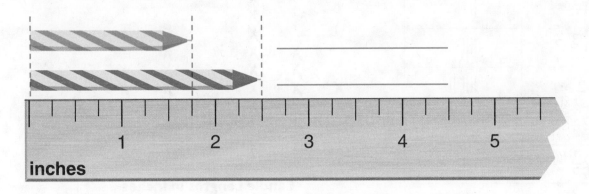

Show how Nina might represent each length on a number line.

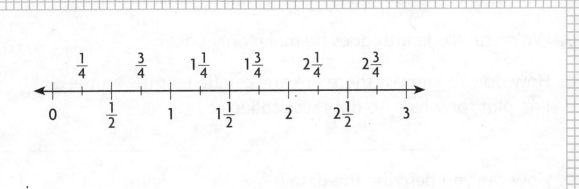

 Turn and Talk How could you show two candles with the same length on a number line?

Build Understanding

1 Kendrick makes candles. He records the number of candles and their lengths in a tally chart. Then he makes a line plot of the data.

Candle Lengths in Inches	
Number of Inches	Tally
$1\frac{1}{2}$	II
$1\frac{3}{4}$	IIII
2	IIII II
$2\frac{1}{4}$	
$2\frac{1}{2}$	IIII
$2\frac{3}{4}$	III
3	I

Candle Lengths in Inches

A. Which candle length does Kendrick make most often? _____

B. Which candle length does he make only once? _____

C. How do you know if there are any candle lengths on the line plot for which no data was collected?

_____

D. How can you describe the data?

_____

_____

Turn and Talk In what ways are the chart and the line plot alike? How are they different?

Step It Out

2 Bob's Candle Shop sells candle wicks with different lengths.

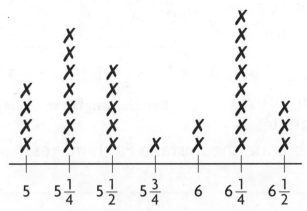

Number of Wicks Sold April 7–14
(Wick Length in Inches)

You can use a line plot to compare data.

A. The shortest wick length is _____ inches.

B. The shop sold _____ of the shortest wick.

C. The longest wick length is _____ inches.

D. The shop sold _____ of the longest wick.

E. Compare the data for the shortest and longest wicks. The shop sold _____ more of the

_____ wick than the _____ wick.

• •

Check Understanding

Use the line plot above.

1 How many wicks did the shop sell? _____

2 The shop sold the most of which wick length? _____

On Your Own

Use the line plot for 3–6.

Faith and Raúl use some candles at a party. After the party, they measure the lengths of the candles.

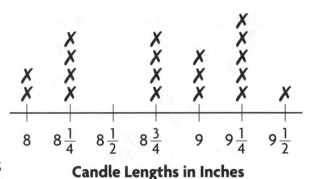

Candle Lengths in Inches

3 (MP) **Critique Reasoning** Faith says the line plot shows that 9 candles have a length of 3 inches. Describe the mistake Faith makes.

_____

_____

_____

4 How many more candles have a length of $9\frac{1}{4}$ inches than a length of 8 inches?

_____

5 How many candles do Faith and Raúl use?

_____

6 **STEM** There are three states of matter: solid, liquid, and gas. The heat from a lit candle makes solid wax become liquid wax. How many candles dripped to a length of less than $8\frac{1}{2}$ inches?

_____

 I'm in a Learning Mindset!

What do I know about line plots?

_____

_____

© Houghton Mifflin Harcourt Publishing Company

Make Line Plots to Display Measurement Data

(I Can) measure lengths to the nearest quarter inch and make a line plot to display the data.

Spark Your Learning

Some students compare the lengths of their used pencils. Measure the length of each pencil to the nearest quarter inch.

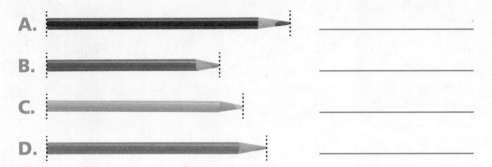

A. _____

B. _____

C. _____

D. _____

Use the number line to record the lengths of the pencils.

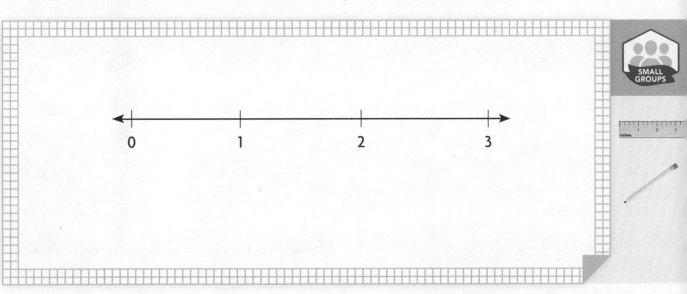

Turn and Talk Do you think if you measure more pencils you might find some pencils with the same lengths measured to the nearest quarter inch? How would the number line change?

Build Understanding

1 You can sort keys by length.

Use a ruler marked with quarter inches. Measure the length of 10 keys to the nearest quarter inch.

Record the data you collect. Then organize your data in a table or tally chart.

 Turn and Talk Share your work. Discuss the different ways you used to organize the data.

Step It Out

2 Use the measurement data that you collected. Make a line plot to show how many times you measured each key length.

A. Write a title below the line.

B. Write numbers or fractions in order, as labels below the number line.

C. Draw an **✗** above the line at each length that matches the data.

For a length that you recorded more than once, make a column of ✗s from bottom to top. Example: ✗

✗

✗

_____

D. Describe your line plot.

_____

_____

· ·

Check Understanding

Use your line plot above.

1 Write a problem about how many more keys have one length than another length. Solve your problem.

_____

_____

On Your Own

2 (MP) **Attend to Precision** Measure and record the length of 10 used crayons to the nearest quarter inch.

- Make a line plot to show the data.

_____

(MP) **Use Structure** **Use your line plot for 3–4.**

3 Which length of crayon appears most often?

_____

4 Describe your line plot in as many ways as you can.

_____

_____

I'm in a Learning Mindset!

What is preventing me from using and making line plots and graphs?

_____

_____

Name

Solve One- and Two-Step Problems Using Data

(I Can) use data in picture graphs, bar graphs, and line plots to solve one- and two-step *how many more* and *how many less* problems.

Step It Out

Favorite Summer Activity	
Activity	**Tally**
Beach	卌 卌
Pool	IIII
Home	卌 IIII
Camp	III
Playground	IIII

1 Pilar surveys the students in her group about their favorite summer activities. How many more students choose beach than pool and camp combined?

A. Make a picture graph of the data.

B. You can use the picture graph to solve the problem. Draw the symbols to compare these rows.

Beach

Think: Beach has a ◐ and ◖ more than pool and camp combined.

Pool Camp

_____	

Key: Each ◐ = 2 students.

What does a half of a symbol stand for

in the graph? _____

C. What equations can you write to find how many more students choose beach than pool and camp combined?

_____

D. _____ more students choose beach than pool and camp combined.

 Turn and Talk What other ways could you display and compare the same data?

Step It Out

2 A store collects data about camping tent sales over 4 months. How many fewer tents were sold in March and April combined than in June?

Camping Tent Sales	
Month	Number Sold
March	10
April	15
May	5
June	50

A. Make a bar graph of the data.

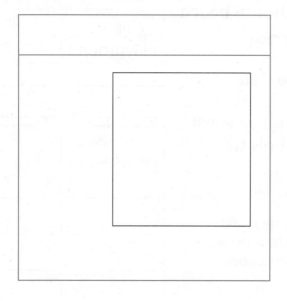

B. One way to solve the problem is to use the bar graph. Compare the bars.

Count back from 50 to 25. Count by 10s and then by 5s.

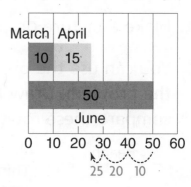

March and April combined

have _____ fewer sales than June.

C. Another way is to draw a bar model and write equations.

10 + 15 = _____

50 − _____ = _____

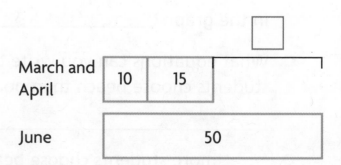

 Turn and Talk How did you know what operations to use to solve each step of the comparison?

3 Cari measures the length of 9 pieces of used chalk to the nearest half inch.

How many more chalk pieces have a length of $1\frac{1}{2}$ inches than lengths of $\frac{1}{2}$ inch and 1 inch combined?

Chalk Lengths in Inches		
$1\frac{1}{2}$ inches	$1\frac{1}{2}$ inches	$\frac{1}{2}$ inch
$2\frac{1}{2}$ inches	$1\frac{1}{2}$ inches	1 inch
1 inch	$1\frac{1}{2}$ inches	$1\frac{1}{2}$ inches

A. Make a line plot to show the data.

_____

B. Use the line plot to solve the problem. Draw *X*s to compare the columns of *X*s.

1 inch $\Big[$ $\Big]$ $1\frac{1}{2}$ inches

$\frac{1}{2}$ inch $\big[$

There are _____ more *X*s.

C. What equations can you write to compare the *X*s? How many more chalk pieces have a length of $1\frac{1}{2}$ inches than lengths of $\frac{1}{2}$ inch and 1 inch combined?

_____

• •

Check Understanding [Math Board]

Use your line plot to answer the questions.

1 How many fewer chalk pieces have a length of 1 inch than lengths of $1\frac{1}{2}$ inches and $2\frac{1}{2}$ inches combined?

2 How many more chalk pieces have a length of $1\frac{1}{2}$ inches than lengths of 1 inch and $2\frac{1}{2}$ inches combined?

© Houghton Mifflin Harcourt Publishing Company

On Your Own

Use the data in the tally chart for 3–7.

A museum collects data about the number of visitors with a museum membership.

Number of Visitors	
Day	**Tally**
Monday	卌 卌 II
Tuesday	IIII
Wednesday	卌 III
Thursday	卌 I
Friday	卌 卌 卌 I

3 (MP) **Attend to Precision** Make a picture graph that shows the data in the table.

4 How many fewer visitors are there on Tuesday than on Thursday and Friday combined?

_____

5 How many more visitors are there on Friday than on Monday?

_____

6 Which day has half of the number of Monday's visitors?

_____

Key: Each _____ = _____.

7 (MP) **Reason** The museum has 12 more visitors with a museum membership on Saturday than on Friday. How many visitors have a museum membership on Saturday? Write an equation you can use to solve the problem. Explain.

_____

_____

_____

Review

Choose the correct term from the Vocabulary box.

1 A _____ is a graph that uses marks to record each piece of data on a number line.

2 A _____ helps to label a graph with equally spaced numbers.

3 A _____ uses symbols to show and compare information.

Concepts and Skills

Use the ribbons for 8–10.

4 (MP) **Use Tools** Measure the length of each ribbon to the nearest quarter inch. Tell what strategy or tool you will use to solve the problem, explain your choice, and then find the answer.

_____

5 Make a line plot that shows the data.

6 How many more ribbons have a length of $1\frac{1}{2}$ inch and 2 inches combined than a length of $\frac{3}{4}$ inch? _____

Use the data in the table for 6–7.

Zoe records in a table the type of animal that students in her class would like to learn how to draw.

7 Make a bar graph that represents the data.

Animal Drawing Choice	
Animal	**Number of Students**
Bear	10
Bird	14
Elephant	12
Horse	20
Lion	18

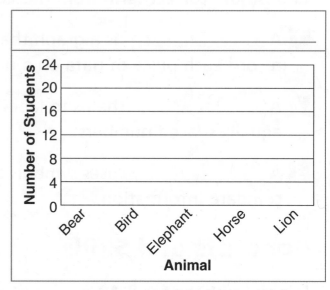

8 How many fewer students choose bear than horse and lion combined?

Ⓐ 10 　　　Ⓑ 28 　　　Ⓒ 38 　　　Ⓓ 48

9 Ms. Kelly collects data about the number of students who attend her art class.

Make a picture graph that shows the data in the tally chart. Choose a number greater than 1 for what the symbol represents.

Number of Students in Art Class	
Month	**Tally**
March	卌 ‖
April	卌
May	卌 卌
June	‖
July	卌 ‖‖

Key: Each _____ = _____.

How many more students attend art class in May than in April and June combined? _____

© Houghton Mifflin Harcourt Publishing Company

Geometry

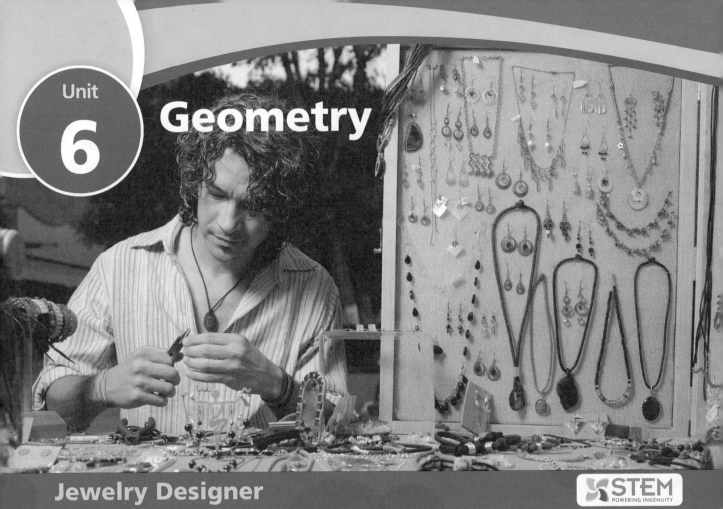

Jewelry Designer

STEM
POWERING INGENUITY

Jewelry designers often use different metals and stones to design works of art that people wear. Jewelry designers have to understand math and science as well as art so that they know what materials to use and how to use them.

Did you know that 100,000 years ago people used items from nature like sea shells and bones to decorate themselves? Then much later, Egyptians began making jewelry using bits of gold that they hammered together. They often used the scarab beetle in their designs and added colorful stones. Egyptians also made glass beads.

STEM Task:

Jewelry designers often make a pattern for a piece of jewelry using geometric shapes such as triangles or rhombuses. Design two shapes for your jewelry using different methods. You can trace pattern blocks or tiles on an index card and cut them out. You can also fold the index card in half and cut out a shape along the fold line. Then draw shapes to represent stones on your cutouts and color them. Tape your stone to a strip of paper to make a bracelet.

Learning Mindset

Perseverance Collects and Tries
Multiple Strategies

It is easy to get frustrated when working on a detail-oriented task like making jewelry. Perseverance is the ability to stick with a task, even if it is difficult. Which strategies do you use when working on a difficult task?

- Take a break and start again.
- Eliminate distractions like noise.
- Try someone else's strategy.
- Use a tool.
- Brainstorm other solutions.

Reflect

Q Which strategy worked best when you were designing your jewelry?

Q What did you learn from this activity that you can apply to other situations?

Define Two-Dimensional Shapes

Which group does **not** belong?

- Look at the groups of shapes.

- An attribute is something that you can use to describe an object, like its color, size, or number of sides. To find the group that does not belong, look for a group that does not have a shared attribute.

A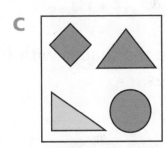

B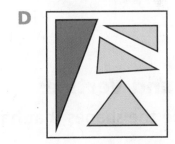

C

D

 Turn and Talk

- How is the group that does not belong different from the other groups?

- What could you change in that group so all the shapes share an attribute?

Are You Ready?

Complete these problems to review prior concepts and skills you will need for this module.

Attributes of Shapes

Write the name of the shape.

1

_____

2

_____

3

_____

Number of Sides

4 Circle the shapes with fewer than 5 sides.

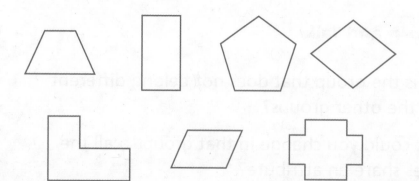

5 Draw two shapes that have more than 3 sides.

Sides and Vertices

6 Circle the shapes that have exactly 4 sides and 4 vertices.

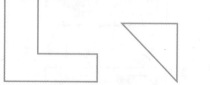

Name

Describe Shapes

(I Can) describe shapes as open or closed, as polygons, and by the number of sides and the number of angles.

Spark Your Learning

Rory uses a 3D printer to make a model of a steel gate for a sculpture garden. She draws this design by using a computer program. When reviewing her work, she sees different shapes within her gate design. What are some shapes that Rory may see?

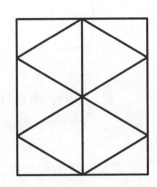

Draw and describe some shapes that Rory may see within the gate.

 Turn and Talk Compare the shapes you found with a classmate. How are your descriptions alike? How are they different?

Build Understanding

1 Shapes *A*, *B*, *C*, and *D* are all alike in one way.

A. Circle the closed shapes. Draw a box around the open shapes.

B. Why are the shapes you circled called closed shapes?

_____

_____

C. Why are the shapes you drew a box around called open shapes?

_____

_____

D. How are shapes *A*, *B*, *C*, and *D* alike?

_____

2 Look at these two shapes.

A. How are they different?

_____

_____

B. Draw a closed shape formed by line segments. Draw an open shape that has at least one curved path.

Connect to Vocabulary

A **closed shape** is a shape that begins and ends at the same point.

An **open shape** is a shape that does not begin and end at the same point.

A **plane shape** is a shape on a flat surface that is formed by curved paths, line segments, or both.

A **line segment** is straight. It is part of a line and has two endpoints.

3 These shapes are alike.

A. What attributes do all the shapes share?

_____

_____

These shapes are all polygons.

B. Draw a polygon. Circle the angles and put an X on the sides.

> **Connect to Vocabulary**
>
> A **polygon** is a closed plane shape with straight sides that are line segments.
>
> Each line segment in a polygon is a **side**.

4 Polygon A has 4 sides and 4 angles. How many sides and angles does Polygon B have?

_____

> **Connect to Vocabulary**
>
> Plane shapes have **angles** formed by two line segments that share an endpoint called a **vertex**.
>
>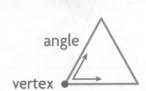
> angle
> vertex

🔄 **Turn and Talk** How is a polygon different from other plane shapes?

Check Understanding 🔲 Math Board

1 Circle the open shape. Put an X on the closed shape.

2 How many sides and angles does this polygon have?

_____

On Your Own

3 (MP) **Critique Reasoning** Dante says that all closed plane shapes are polygons. Is Dante correct? Explain your answer.

_____

_____

_____

4 **Social Studies** Mya uses a map to study some of the western states in the United States. Some states have a border in the shape of a polygon. Name one state that could be in the shape of a polygon. Explain how you know.

_____

_____

Is the shape a polygon? Write _yes_ or _no_.

5

_____

6

_____

7

_____

Write the number of sides and the number of angles.

8 _____ sides

_____ angles

9 _____ sides

_____ angles

I'm in a Learning Mindset!

What helps me remember the names of different attributes of shapes?

_____

Name _____

Describe Angles in Shapes

(**I Can**) identify angles that are right angles, greater than a right angle, or less than a right angle in shapes.

Spark Your Learning

Felix wrote this riddle:

I am a closed shape with at least 3 angles and 3 sides. My sides are not all equal in length, but all my angles are equal. What shape am I?

Draw and name a shape to solve the riddle.

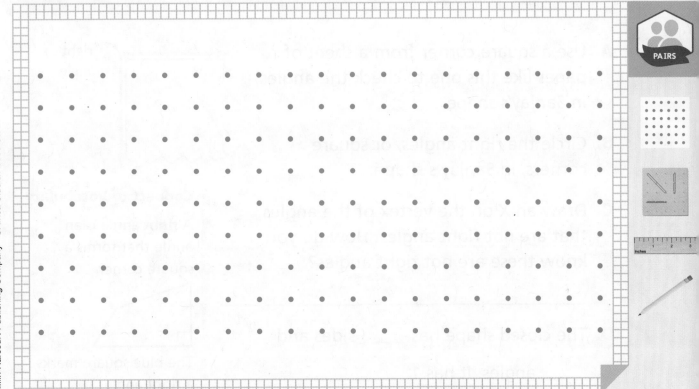

Turn and Talk Help Felix write another riddle that describes a shape. What shape does the riddle describe? Why does this shape solve the riddle?

Build Understanding

1 Sanjay makes a coloring book with different shapes to color. One of the shapes is shown below. How can you describe the angles of this shape?

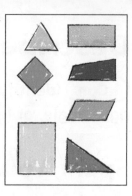

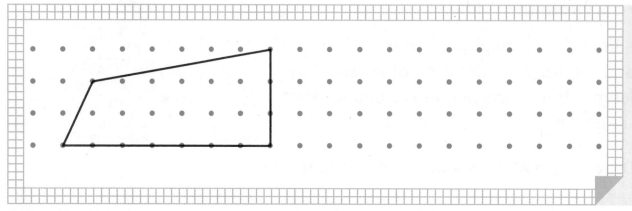

A. Use a square corner from a sheet of paper like this one to check the angles in Sanjay's shape.

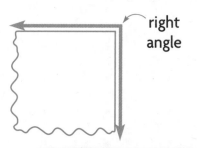
right angle

B. Circle the right angles, or square corners, in Sanjay's shape.

C. Draw an X on the vertex of the angles that are not right angles. How do you know these are not right angles?

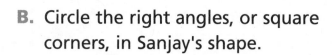

D. The closed shape has _____ sides and

_____ angles. It has 1 _____

and _____ angles that are not right angles.

Connect to Vocabulary

A **right angle** is an angle that forms a square corner.

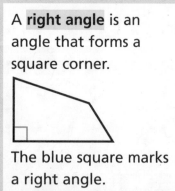

The blue square marks a right angle.

 Turn and Talk Are all right angles the same? Explain.

Name _____

2 The blue angles are right angles.

- The red angle is greater than a right angle.

- The yellow angle is less than a right angle.

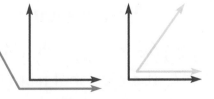

Use a square corner to compare the angles in the shapes to a right angle.

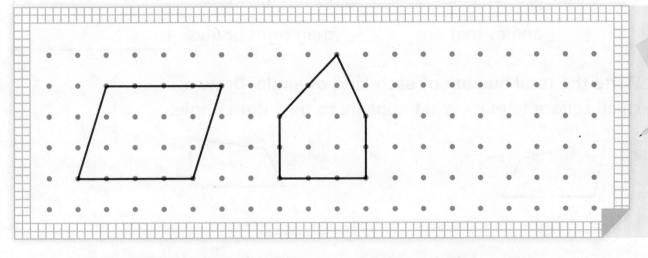

A. Draw a small square to show each right angle.

B. Draw a circle around the vertex of each angle that is greater than a right angle. Shade the vertex of each angle that is less than a right angle.

C. Draw a shape that has exactly 3 right angles in the work space above.

· ·

Check Understanding [Math Board]

Write _right angle_, _greater than a right angle_, or _less than a right angle_ for the blue angle.

1

2

3

_____   _____

On Your Own

4 **(MP)** **Reason** Tim cuts a rectangular tile on the diagonal from the top left to the bottom right corners.

- Before the cut, there are _____ right angles.

- After the cut, there are _____ right angles and

  _____ angles that are _____ than right angles.

Write the total number of each kind of angle. Draw a small square to mark what appears to be a right angle.

5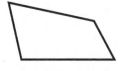

_____ right

_____ less than right

_____ greater than right

6

_____ right

_____ less than right

_____ greater than right

7 **STEM** The incoming and outgoing angles of a reflected light beam are always equal. Angle *A* is formed by the reflected light beam. Is Angle *A* a right angle, greater than a right angle, or less than a right angle?

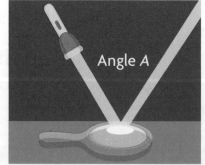

Angle A

_____

© Houghton Mifflin Harcourt Publishing Company • ©age fotostock/Alamy

⬡ I'm in a Learning Mindset!

How effective is using a corner of a sheet of paper to identify right angles and other angles? Explain.

_____

Name _____

Describe Sides of Shapes

(I Can) identify whether the sides of a shape are equal or
not equal in length. I can identify parallel sides of a shape.

Spark Your Learning

Anya draws plans *A* and *B* for a 4-sided tabletop
she is making.

Describe the sides of each tabletop design.

A

B

PAIRS

Blue sides

Length: _____

_____

Distance apart: _____

_____

Red sides

Length: _____

_____

Distance apart: _____

_____

Blue sides

Length: _____

_____

Distance apart: _____

_____

Red sides

Length: _____

_____

Distance apart: _____

_____

Turn and Talk Compare how the sides of plans
A and *B* are alike and how they are different.

499

Build Understanding

1 Emma draws shapes *A*, *B*, and *C*. Which shape has 3 sides that are equal in length?

Compare the lengths of the sides.

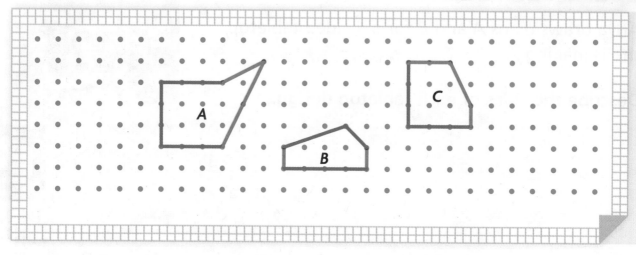

A. Which sides of shape *A* are equal in length? How do you know?

_____

_____

B. Which sides of shape *B* are equal in length? How do you know?

_____

_____

C. Which sides of shape *C* are equal in length? How do you know?

_____

_____

 Turn and Talk Can all sides of a 4-sided shape be equal in length? Explain how you know.

Name

2 Emma draws shapes *D* and *E*.

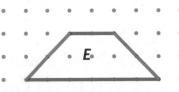

A. Which sides of shape D are
the same distance apart and
appear to be parallel? Explain.

_____

_____

_____

Connect to Vocabulary

Lines in the same plane
that never cross and
are always the same
distance apart are
parallel lines.
The red sides
are parallel.

B. Which sides of shape *E* appear to
be parallel? Which sides are not
parallel? Explain how you know.

_____

_____

 Turn and Talk Can a 3-sided shape have parallel
sides? Explain.

. . . .

Check Understanding [Math Board]

1 Draw a line to match the shape to the words that describe
the red sides.

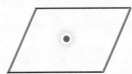   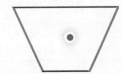

not parallel,
equal in length

not parallel,
not equal
in length

appear to be
parallel, equal
in length

On Your Own

2 (MP) **Critique Reasoning** Li says a shape cannot have 4 sides of equal length and 2 pairs of parallel sides. Is Li correct? Explain and draw an example to show your thinking.

_____

_____

Write *equal length* or *not equal length* to describe the green sides of the shape.

3

4

5

_____

Look at the green sides of the shape. Write if they appear to be *parallel* or *not parallel*.

6

7

8

_____   _____   _____

9 **Open Ended** Write a riddle about a closed shape with 4 sides. Tell whether the sides are equal in length and whether any sides are parallel.

_____

_____

✦ I'm in a Learning Mindset!

Did I try a new strategy that my partner suggested? What was it?

_____

Name

Define Quadrilaterals

(I Can) use the number of sides, the number of angles, the number of sides of equal length, and the number of right angles to describe and identify quadrilaterals.

Spark Your Learning

Misty is making a sign for the Green Star Mountain Climbing Club. The club has asked for a sign that is a 4-sided polygon with exactly 2 right angles.

Draw a polygon Misty could use.

Turn and Talk What polygons could Misty use if the sign is a 4-sided polygon with *at least* 2 right angles? Explain.

Build Understanding

1 How can you use attributes to name and identify
quadrilaterals? Circle all the attributes the shapes share.

A. 4 sides   4 angles   4 right angles

2 pairs of opposite sides of equal length

4 sides of equal length

At least 1 pair of parallel sides

2 pairs of parallel sides

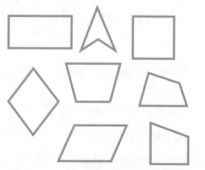

These are **quadrilaterals**.

B. 4 sides   4 angles   4 right angles

2 pairs of opposite sides of equal length

4 sides of equal length

At least 1 pair of parallel sides

2 pairs of parallel sides

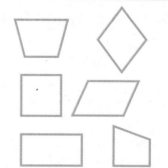

These are **trapezoids**.

C. 4 sides   4 angles   4 right angles

2 pairs of opposite sides of equal length

4 sides of equal length

At least 1 pair of parallel sides

2 pairs of parallel sides

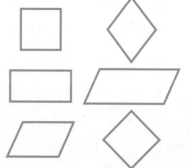

These are **parallelograms**.

 Turn and Talk A trapezoid can also be defined as a
quadrilateral that has *exactly* 1 pair of parallel sides.
Shade all the shapes above that match this definition.
Describe these shapes.

D. 4 sides   4 angles   4 right angles

2 pairs of opposite sides of equal length

4 sides of equal length

At least 1 pair of parallel sides

2 pairs of parallel sides

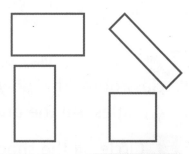

These are **rectangles**.

E. 4 sides   4 angles   4 right angles

2 pairs of opposite sides of equal length

4 sides of equal length

At least 1 pair of parallel sides

2 pairs of parallel sides

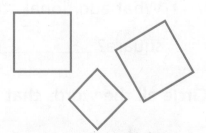

These are **squares**.

F. 4 sides   4 angles   4 right angles

2 pairs of opposite sides of equal length

4 sides of equal length

At least 1 pair of parallel sides

2 pairs of parallel sides

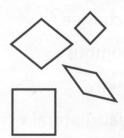

These are **rhombuses**.

Check Understanding Math Board

1 Write the letters that match the shape.

Define a trapezoid as a quadrilateral that has *at least* 1 pair of parallel sides.

  A

  B

  C

Rectangle _____   Quadrilateral _____   Trapezoid _____

Rhombus _____   Parallelogram _____   Square _____

On Your Own

2 (MP) **Reason** Max sees a polygon in his classroom. This polygon has 4 sides and 4 angles. All the angles are right angles.

Define a trapezoid as a quadrilateral that has *exactly* 1 pair of parallel sides.

- Circle all the shapes the polygon could be.

  rectangle   rhombus   triangle   hexagon   square   trapezoid

- What additional attribute would make the polygon a

  square? _____

Circle all the words that describe the quadrilateral.

3

rectangle

rhombus

square

quadrilateral

4

parallelogram

rectangle

square

rhombus

5

parallelogram

trapezoid

square

rectangle

(MP) **Reason** Write *all* or *some* to complete the sentences.

6 _____ the sides of a square are equal in length.

7 _____ rhombuses are squares.

8 _____ sides of a rectangle are of equal length.

9 _____ squares are rectangles.

I'm in a Learning Mindset!

What strategies for describing quadrilaterals did I share with my partner?

_____

Review

Vocabulary

Choose the correct term from the Vocabulary box to complete the sentence.

Vocabulary
closed shape line segment open shape right angle vertex

1 A _____ is an angle that forms a square corner.

2 Each side in a polygon is a _____.

Concepts and Skills

3 (MP) **Use Tools** Select all the shapes that appear to have a right angle. Tell what strategy or tool you will use to solve the problem, explain your choice, and then find the answers.

_____

Ⓐ    Ⓒ    Ⓔ

Ⓑ 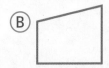   Ⓓ   Ⓕ

4 Write *polygon* or *not a polygon* to describe the shape.

_____   _____   _____

5 Write the number of sides and the number of angles for this shape.

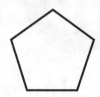

_____

6 Draw a polygon that has exactly 3 sides and exactly 3 angles.

7 A square and a rhombus are shown.

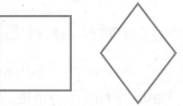

Select all the attributes that these shapes *always* have in common.

Ⓐ number of sides   Ⓓ angles greater than a right angle

Ⓑ number of angles   Ⓔ angles less than a right angle

Ⓒ right angle   Ⓕ all sides are of equal length

8 When a trapezoid is defined as a quadrilateral that has *exactly* 1 pair of sides the same distance apart, what shape is always a quadrilateral and never a parallelogram?

Ⓐ rhombus   Ⓒ square

Ⓑ rectangle   Ⓓ trapezoid

9 When a trapezoid is defined as a quadrilateral that has *at least* 1 pair of sides the same distance apart, select all the words that can describe a square.

Ⓐ parallelogram   Ⓒ rectangle   Ⓔ triangle

Ⓑ trapezoid   Ⓓ quadrilateral   Ⓕ rhombus

Can **you** find the **mystery shape**?

- Read the list of clues.

- Use the clues to identify the mystery shape.

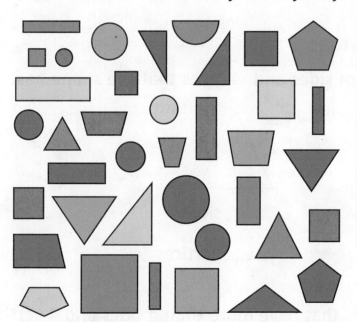

Clues:

- I am formed with only line segments.

- I have exactly four vertices.

- Exactly three of my sides have the same length.

What is the mystery shape? _____

 Turn and Talk

- Are there any other shapes that match the description in the third clue? Explain.

- How did you decide that the shape you chose fit all of the clues?

Are You Ready?

Complete these problems to review prior concepts and skills you will need for this module.

Draw Two-Dimensional Shapes

1 Draw a rectangle.

2 Draw a trapezoid.

Sides and Vertices

Write the number of sides and vertices that the shape has.

3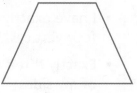

_____ sides

_____ vertices

4

_____ sides

_____ vertices

5

_____ sides

_____ vertices

6 Circle the shapes that have more than 4 sides and 4 vertices.

   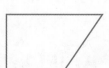

Name

Draw Quadrilaterals

(**I Can**) draw a quadrilateral given descriptions of the sides and angles in the shape. I can group quadrilaterals using the side lengths or number of right angles.

Spark Your Learning

An architect is asked to design an outdoor theater stage in the shape of a quadrilateral. The stage must have 2 pairs of parallel sides, no right angles, and at least 2 sides that are different in length.

Draw a design that the architect could use.

Turn and Talk How would the architect's design change if the stage has only 1 pair of parallel sides?

Build Understanding

1 Draw a quadrilateral that has 2 pairs of opposite sides that are equal in length, 2 pairs of opposite parallel sides, and 4 right angles.

A. To which quadrilateral categories does the shape you drew belong?

_____

B. How do you know the shape you drew belongs to those categories?

_____

_____

_____

2 Look at the quadrilaterals.

A. What name do all of the quadrilaterals in this group share?

_____

B. Draw a quadrilateral that does not belong to this group. Explain why this shape does not belong to the group.

_____

_____

 Turn and Talk Compare your drawing from Task 2 with a classmate. Do both drawings belong to the same group? Why or why not?

3 Look at the shapes.

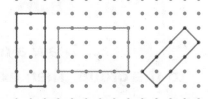

A. What name do all the quadrilaterals in this group share?

_____

B. Draw a shape that belongs to this group.

C. What attributes do all the shapes in this group share?

_____

_____

4 Look at the shapes.

A. Draw shape *A* that belongs to the group.

B. Draw shape *B* that has 2 right angles and exactly one pair of parallel sides.

Turn and Talk What quadrilateral group do both shape *A* and shape *B* above belong to? Explain.

Check Understanding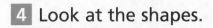

Draw and name the quadrilateral.

1 4 sides of equal length, no right angles

2 2 pairs of parallel sides, no right angles

On Your Own

 Reason Draw a quadrilateral that does not belong to the group. Then explain why it does not belong.

3

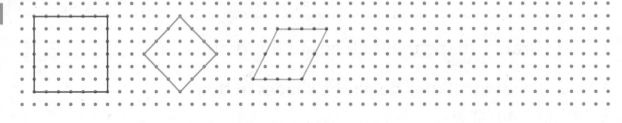

_____

_____

4

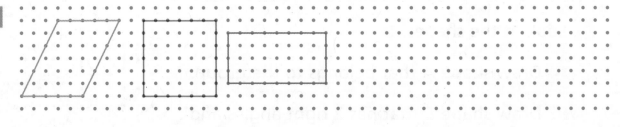

_____

_____

5 **Reason** Rhombus Billboards makes all their signs in the shape of a rhombus. On April Fool's Day, Rhombus Billboards makes a quadrilateral sign that is not a rhombus. Draw a sign that the company might make. Explain why the shape you drew does not belong in the group. _____

_____

 I'm in a Learning Mindset!

Do I share and accept strategies from others? What are some examples?

_____

Name _____

Categorize Quadrilaterals

(I Can) identify whether a shape belongs in a group by the number of sides, number of angles, sides that are equal in length, parallel sides, and by some shape names and attributes.

Spark Your Learning

Sydney uses computer programing to draw a quadrilateral that has at least one pair of parallel sides.

Draw three or more shapes that the computer might draw.

Turn and Talk Sydney now codes a program to draw a quadrilateral with four sides of equal length and at least one right angle. What quadrilateral will the computer draw? Explain how you know.

Build Understanding

1 Place the quadrilaterals into the correct categories. Some shapes may belong to more than one category.

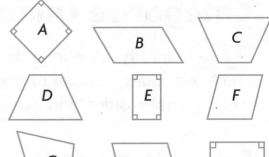

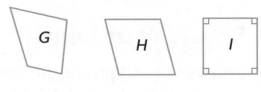

A. Quadrilaterals: _____

How do you know that a shape is a quadrilateral?

_____

B. Rhombuses: _____

How do you know that a shape is a rhombus?

_____

C. Parallelograms: _____

How do you know that a shape is a parallelogram?

_____

D. Trapezoids that are defined as having *exactly* one

pair of parallel sides: _____

How do you know that a shape is a trapezoid?

_____

E. Rectangles: _____

How do you know that a shape is a rectangle?

_____

_____

 Turn and Talk How would your answer in Part D change if a trapezoid is defined as having *at least* one pair of parallel sides?

2 Circle the words that describe the shape.

Define a trapezoid as a quadrilateral that has *at least* one pair of parallel sides.

parallelogram

quadrilateral

rectangle

rhombus

trapezoid

square

parallelogram

quadrilateral

rectangle

rhombus

trapezoid

square

parallelogram

quadrilateral

rectangle

rhombus

trapezoid

square

 Turn and Talk Which shape belongs to the most categories? What attributes help to explain this?

Check Understanding

Math Board

Circle the words that describe the shape. Define a trapezoid as a quadrilateral that has *exactly* one pair of parallel sides.

1

2

3

parallelogram

quadrilateral

rectangle

rhombus

trapezoid

square

parallelogram

quadrilateral

rectangle

rhombus

trapezoid

square

parallelogram

quadrilateral

rectangle

rhombus

trapezoid

square

On Your Own

4 (MP) **Construct Arguments** Explain why a rectangle is always a parallelogram, but a parallelogram is not always a rectangle.

_____

_____

5 (MP) **Reason** Is a square always a rectangle? How do you know?

_____

_____

Is a rectangle always a square? How do you know?

_____

6 **STEM** Crystals can form when liquid rock under Earth cools and hardens into a pattern. What quadrilateral best describes one of the crystal's faces that has 4 sides of equal length and 2 pairs of parallel sides?

_____

7 Circle the shapes that are trapezoids when a trapezoid is defined as a quadrilateral that has *exactly* one pair of parallel sides.

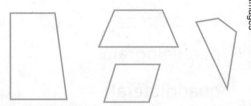

 I'm in a Learning Mindset!

What do I do when I do not know how to classify a quadrilateral?

_____

Name _____

Categorize Plane Shapes

(I Can) identify whether a plane shape belongs in a category by the number of parallel sides, sides of equal length, and right angles.

Spark Your Learning

Louise and Paul play a game that has cards with shapes on them. Each shape in the game represents a different move on the game board. How can Louise and Paul sort the shapes below?

Show one way to sort the shapes by their attributes.

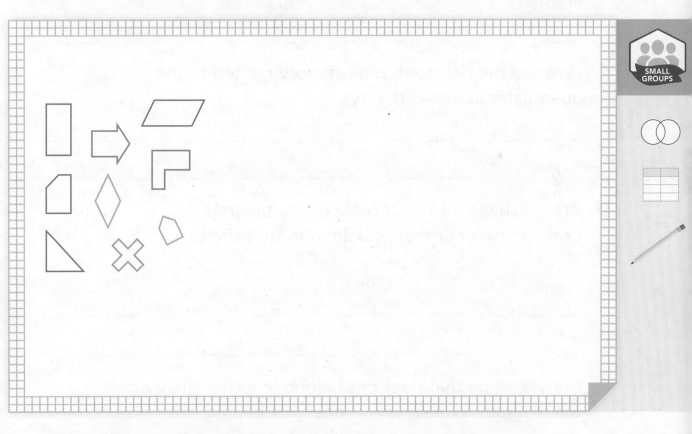

 Turn and Talk Describe another way in which Louise and Paul could sort the shapes. Explain how the ways to sort the shapes are the same and different.

Build Understanding

1 Louise and Paul use a Venn diagram to sort shapes.

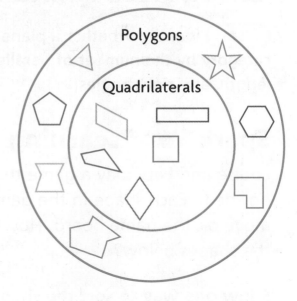

Polygons

Quadrilaterals

A. How are the polygons within the outer circle of the diagram related to one another?

_____

_____

B. How are the quadrilaterals within the inner circle related to one another?

_____

C. How are the polygons as a category related to the quadrilaterals as a category?

_____

_____

D. Draw a shape into each circle of the diagram. Explain how your shapes belong in that circle.

_____

_____

_____

E. Draw a shape that does not belong in either circle of the diagram. Explain why it does not belong.

_____

 Turn and Talk Is a quadrilateral always a polygon? Is a polygon always a quadrilateral? Explain.

2 Here is a group of plane shapes.

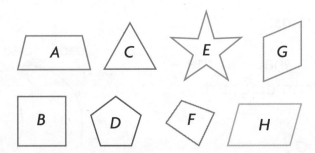

A. Which of the plane shapes are quadrilaterals? Write the letter of the shape.

_____

B. Which of the plane shapes are polygons with all sides of equal length? Write the letter of the shape.

_____

C. Use the Venn diagram to sort and compare the shapes. Label each circle of the diagram. Place the letter of each shape in the diagram.

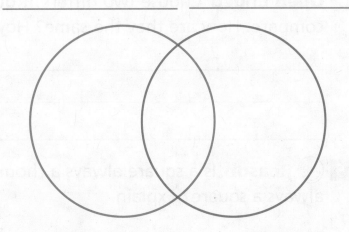

• •

Check Understanding

1 Circle the plane shapes that are polygons with exactly one pair of equal-length sides. Draw a line through the shapes that appear to have exactly one pair of parallel sides.

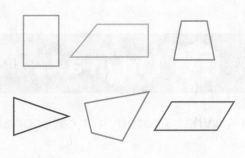

On Your Own

Complete the Venn diagrams.

2 Place the letter of each shape in the correct place in the Venn diagram.

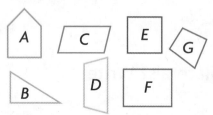

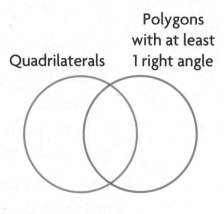

Quadrilaterals / Polygons with at least 1 right angle

3 Place the letter of each shape in the correct place in the Venn diagram.

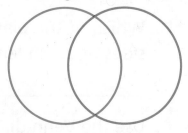

Rectangles / Rhombuses

4 **Open Ended** Choose two different quadrilaterals to compare. How are they the same? How are they different?

_____

_____

_____

5 **Reason** Is a square always a rhombus? Is a rhombus always a square? Explain.

_____

_____

I'm in a Learning Mindset!

What strategy for categorizing plane shapes have I not yet tried?

_____

Name

Review

Vocabulary

1 Draw lines to match the shape to the correct term.

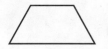

• trapezoid

Define a trapezoid as a quadrilateral that has *exactly* one pair of parallel sides.

• rhombus

Concepts and Skills

2 Draw a quadrilateral that is not a square.

3 (MP) **Use Tools** Draw a quadrilateral that has *exactly* 2 right angles. Tell what strategy or tool you will use to solve the problem and explain your choice.

© Houghton Mifflin Harcourt Publishing Company

4 Select all the words that describe this shape.

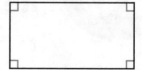

Ⓐ parallelogram   Ⓓ square

Ⓑ quadrilateral   Ⓔ polygon

Ⓒ rhombus   Ⓕ rectangle

5 Select all the shapes that are polygons and have *exactly* one pair of sides of equal length.

Ⓐ

Ⓓ

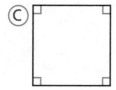

Ⓑ

Ⓔ

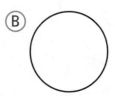

Ⓒ

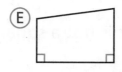

Ⓕ

6 Select all the shapes that can be placed in the part of the diagram where the circles overlap.

Ⓐ square

Ⓑ rectangle

Ⓒ trapezoid

Ⓓ parallelogram

Ⓔ rhombus

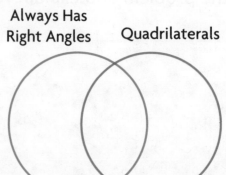

Always Has Right Angles   Quadrilaterals

A

addition

doubles, 62, 64, 66

equations for, 293, 295, 297, 298

expanded form, 270–272

measurement

liquid volume and mass, 448, 450

perimeter, 304–306, 307–310, 311–314, 315–318, 319–322

time intervals, 335–338, 339–342, 343–346

mental math strategies, 245–248, 253–256

with partial sums, 271–272

patterns, 211–214, 241–244

by place value, 270–272, 273–278, 289–292

properties of

Associative Property of Addition, 250–252

Commutative Property of Addition, 242–244

Identity Property of Addition, 242–244

reasonableness of answer, 253–256

regroup to add, 274–278

relate to multiplication, 9–12, 43–46

repeated, 9–12

addition table, 241–244

algebra

addition

doubles, 62, 64, 66

equations for, 293, 295, 297, 298

expanded form, 270–272

mental math strategies, 245–248, 253–256

patterns, 211–214, 241–244

by place value, 270–272, 273–278, 289–292

properties of

Associative Property of Addition, 250–252

Commutative Property of Addition, 242–244

Identity Property of Addition, 242–244

reasonableness of answer, 253–256

regroup to add, 274–278

repeated, 9–12

area

of combined rectangles, 51–54

compare to perimeter, 315–318, 319–322

count unit squares for, 35–38, 39–42, 43–46, 51–54

defined, 37

and fractions, 385–388, 389–392, 393–396

of rectangles, 43–46, 47–50, 51–54

relate to addition and multiplication, 43–46

division

equal groups and, 139–142, 143–146, 147–150, 155–158, 159–162

fluency, 203–206

one- and two-step problems with, 215–220, 221–224, 225–230, 231–234

rules, 163–166

with unknown numbers, 215–220, 221–224, 225–230, 231–234

equations

for doubles, 62–66

expanded form, 270–272

multiplication, 11

for perimeter, 304–306, 307–310, 311–314, 315–318, 319–322

two-step problems and, 225–230, 293–298

multiplication

with arrays, 13–16, 17–20, 92–94, 96–98, 196, 198, 200

equal groups and, 5–8, 9–12, 13–16, 17–20, 60, 62–63, 65, 70, 74, 77–78, 82, 99, 172–173, 175–176, 180

fluency, 203–206

on a multiplication table, 76, 78, 107–112, 113

one- and two-step problems with, 215–220, 221–224, 225–230, 231–234

patterns, 211–214

properties of

Associative Property of Multiplication, 91–94, 123–126, 249–252

Index

numerator, 362, 409–412, 413–416
unit fractions, 358–360, 393–396
whole numbers as, 369–372

fractions greater than 1, 374–376

geometry
angles, 493, 495–498
attributes of two-dimensional shapes,
491–494, 495–498, 499–502, 503–506,
511–514, 515–518, 519–522
closed shape, 492–494
line segment, 492
open shape, 492–494, 519
parallel lines, 501
partition shapes into equal areas,
389–392
plane shape, 492
polygon, 493
quadrilateral, 503–506, 511–514,
515–518, 520–522
side, 493
vertex, 493

Glossary. *See More Practice and
Homework Journal*

gram (g), 444–446, 448–452

graphs. *See data*

grouping. *See Associative Property
of Addition; Associative Property of
Multiplication*

groups, equal
arrays and, 13–16, 17–20, 92–94, 96–98,
155–158, 186, 196, 198, 200
count, 5–8
defined, 6
division and, 139–142, 143–146, 147–150,
155–158, 159–162, 163–164, 172–173,
175–176, 179–181, 185, 191–192, 197,
203–204
multiplication and, 5–8, 9–12, 13–16,
17–20, 60, 62–63, 65, 70, 74, 77–78, 82,
99, 172–173, 175–176, 180

growing pattern, 212–214, 235

half hour, 339–340

half inch, 377–380, 473–476, 477–480

halves, 355

horizontal bar graph, 467

hour, 328–330

how many more **and** ***less*** **problems**
bar graphs for, 465–468, 469–472, 482
picture graphs for, 457–460, 461–464,
481, 484

hundreds
expanded form, 270–272
regroup, 132–134, 273–278, 279–282,
283–288, 289–292

Identity Property of Addition, 242–244

Identity Property of Multiplication,
83–86

inch, 377–380, 473–476, 477–480

intervals of time, 335–338, 339–342,
343–346

inverse operations
facts and, 175–178, 179–184, 185–190,
191–196, 197–202
for fluency, 203–206
represent, 172–174

key, for picture graph, 458–460

kilogram (kg), 444–446

length
measure, 377–380, 473–476, 477–480
unknown perimeter side lengths,
312–314

line plots, 473–476, 477–480, 481–483

© Houghton Mifflin Harcourt Publishing Company

Index

line segment, 492
lines, parallel, 501
liquid volume, 440–442, 447, 450–452
liter (L), 440–442, 447, 450–452

M

manipulatives and materials
  addition table, 241–243
  analog clock, 327–328, 331–332, 335–336
  bar graph, 465–468, 469–470, 482
  bar model, 25–30, 70, 73, 99, 103,
    159–162, 171–173, 176, 185, 191,
    197, 202, 216–217, 245, 249–250,
    253–254, 261
  base-ten blocks, 127–128, 131–132, 249,
    253, 269–270, 273, 279, 283, 289, 469
  clock, 327–328, 331–332, 335–336
  coins, 67–68
  connecting cubes, 5–7, 9–11, 25–26, 107,
    127–128, 139, 141, 143–145, 147–148,
    151, 155, 159–161, 163, 172–173,
    175–176, 179, 197, 203, 241, 469
  fraction circle, 361, 369, 373, 401–402,
    405, 409–410, 413–414
  fraction rectangle, 365, 406, 414
  fraction strip, 369, 401, 405–406,
    409–410, 413–414, 421–422, 425
  geoboard, 495, 500, 511, 515
  grid paper, 18–19, 35, 47–48, 117, 171,
    197, 307, 358, 386, 393–394, 402
  line plot, 473–476, 479–480, 481–483
  money, 67–68
  number line, 5–6, 9–11, 21–23, 61–62,
    67, 73, 95, 99–100, 103, 127–128, 140,
    152–153, 159, 171, 179, 185, 191,
    197, 203, 246, 249–250, 254, 257–258,
    261–262, 332, 335, 365, 405–406,
    409–410, 425, 477
  pan balance, 443–444
  pattern blocks, 393, 491
  picture graph, 457–460, 461–464
  place-value chart, 245, 249–250, 254,
    257–258, 261–262, 269–270, 289
  ruler, 21, 307–308, 377, 393–394, 473,
    477–478, 491, 495, 499, 503

  square dot paper, 491, 495, 499–500,
    503, 511, 515, 519
  square tile, 13–15, 17–19, 21, 35, 40,
    47–48, 61–62, 73, 83–84, 87, 91, 95,
    99, 103, 139–141, 143–145, 147–148,
    151, 155–157, 163, 171, 175, 179, 191,
    215–217, 241, 305, 307–308, 357, 469
  two-color counter, 5–7, 9–11, 13, 17,
    25–26, 35, 61–62, 67–68, 74, 83–84, 87,
    91, 95, 107, 139–141, 143–145, 147–148,
    151, 160–161, 163, 172, 175–176, 185,
    203, 211, 216–217, 461–462
  Venn diagram, 519–522

mass, 443–446, 447–452

Mathematical Practices and Processes
  1. *make sense of problems and persevere
    in solving them,* occurs throughout.
    Some examples are 14, 21, 40, 61, 110,
    127, 151, 185–186, 225–227, 231–232,
    241, 254, 261, 270, 279, 293–295, 312,
    315, 339, 369, 373, 390, 401, 425
  2. *reason abstractly and quantitatively,*
    in some lessons. Some examples are
    29, 38, 50, 71, 188
  3. *construct viable arguments and
    critique the reasoning of others,* in
    some lessons. Some examples are 42,
    121, 126, 130, 142
  4. *model with mathematics,* in some
    lessons. Some examples are 12, 16, 20,
    24, 29
  5. *use appropriate tools strategically,* in
    some lessons. Some examples are 8,
    65, 71, 112, 162
  6. *attend to precision,* in some lessons.
    Some examples are 16, 42, 46, 54, 146
  7. *look for and make use of structure,* in
    some lessons. Some examples are 12,
    78, 90, 98, 102
  8. *look for and express regularity in
    repeated reasoning,* in some lessons.
    Some examples are 46, 72, 111, 122

Math on the Spot videos, some lessons
feature a Math on the Spot video
problem. *See also* student and parent
resources on Ed: Your Friend in Learning.

S